Scotland's leading educational publishers

#1 FOR REVISION

National 5
BIOLOGY
SUCCESS GUIDE

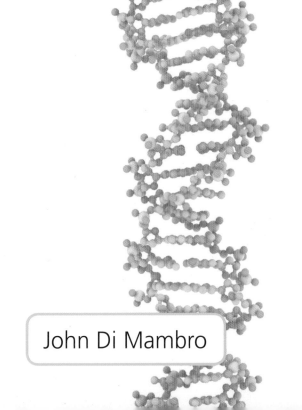

N5 BIOLOGY SUCCESS GUIDE

John Di Mambro

001/27092013

10 9 8 7 6 5 4 3 2 1

ISBN 9780007504688

Published by
Leckie & Leckie Ltd
An imprint of HarperCollins*Publishers*
Westerhill Road, Bishopbriggs, Glasgow, G64 2QT
T: 0844 576 8126   F: 0844 576 8131
leckieandleckie@harpercollins.co.uk   www.leckieandleckie.co.uk

Special thanks to
QBS (layout and illustration); Jan Fisher (copy editing); Alistair Coats (proofreading and project management)

A CIP Catalogue record for this book is available from the British Library.

Dedication
For Gordon M. Buchanan, one of the finest students I have encountered in my teaching career.

Acknowledgements
We would like to thank the following for permission to reproduce their material:
Knorre (p.33, 107), Keith Brofsky (p.47), F. JIMENEZ MECA (p.52), Jupiterimages (p.53, 89), Stockbyte (p.68, 78, 87), Photography-ByMK (p.69), Comstock Images (p.69, 106), Anup Shah (p.78, 86), Ryan McVay (p.79), NIGEL CATTLIN/SCIENCE PHOTO LIBRARY (p.84), Tom Brakefield (p.86), Chris Howes/Wild Places Photography / Alamy (p.88), PHILIPPE PSAILA/SCIENCE PHOTO LIBRARY (p.89), Cosmin Manci (p.93), Creatas Images (p.94), Hemera Technologies (p.95), Nicku (p.96), MICHAEL W. TWEEDIE/ SCIENCE PHOTO LIBRARY (p.97), DR KEITH WHEELER/SCIENCE PHOTO LIBRARY (p.107), THOMAS AMES JR., VISUALS UNLIMITED /SCIENCE PHOTO LIBRARY (p.107), Cray Photo (p.108), WAYNE LAWLER/SCIENCE PHOTO LIBRARY (p.108), jirapong (p.110)

Unit 1 – Cell Biology

Contents

Unit 2 – Multicellular organisms

Unit 3 – Life on Earth

Introduction

This book has been written primarily as a revision guide for the new National 5 qualification in Biology. It covers all the content of the course, following the national syllabus exactly, in a very user-friendly way. Topics are usually displayed in double-page spreads with many topics taking up several double-page spreads. Information is presented in 'bite-sized' chunks and illustrated with appropriate graphics to enhance your understanding and learning. Remember that Biology is a very visual science! Top tips will appear frequently. These are based on many years' experience teaching students not only what to learn but also how to learn in Biology. Topics have 'Quick Tests' and answers. Each unit has a more global set of questions called 'End of Unit Questions' which include problem-solving. There are objective style and short and longer response questions. Answers to these unit tests are also provided. These are very powerful ways of giving feedback on how well you have a mastered a section of the course. In addition, all eight of the 'scientific inquiry skills' specified by The Scottish Qualification Authority are tested. A comprehensive glossary is included and an excellent idea would be to make flash-cards of these terms using readily available and free software from the Internet.

With any revision programme, it is essential to make a good and early start and be self-disciplined enough to follow this through. Every student's study and revision strategies are different and it is important that you look carefully at how you learn. If your strategies are not producing the results you would expect, then revisit them and try out some ideas. Talk these over with your teacher and friends. Engage with your learning and don't just 'read over your notes', one of the poorest forms of revision and consolidation. Critically, if you hit a problem, discuss this as soon as possible with your teacher to resolve it before it escalates into an issue which might impact seriously on your final award. Above all, be thorough!

Guidance on the examination

The actual final examination paper assesses your knowledge-base across all of the Units. In addition, it will assess eight different skills that are, in general terms, inquiry, analytical thinking as well as the impact of applications on society and the environment. The full detailed list of these skills is available from the Scottish Qualifications Authority's website.

The final question paper contributes 80% of the total mark you can achieve and has two sections:

Section 1 has objective style questions and is worth 20 marks

Section 2 has short and longer response questions and is worth 60 marks

The examiners will ensure the marks available are distributed proportionally across the whole course which reinforces the need to have a global command of the syllabus.

Approximately 55 marks are for knowledge and understanding and approximately 25 marks are for applying scientific inquiring skills.

The other 20% of the total mark you can achieve comes from a combination of an 'in-house' investigation, report and problem-solving paper. These are assessed internally by your teacher.

Cell structure

Basic cell structure

TOP TIP

When drawing diagrams in Biology, don't use arrowed-headed lines and make sure the lines end exactly on the structure you are labelling.

Under a light microscope, you can see that living things are made up of cells, which share similar structures: **cell membrane**, **cytoplasm** and **nucleus**. Green plant cells have additional features: **chloroplasts**, **vacuole** and **cell wall**.

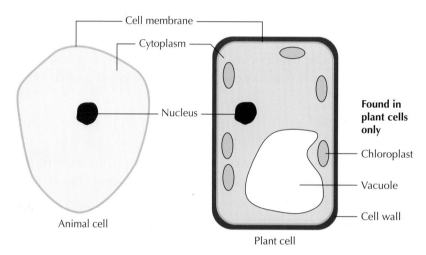

Cell membrane

Cytoplasm

Nucleus

Animal cell

Found in plant cells only

Chloroplast

Vacuole

Cell wall

Plant cell

Cell structure	Function
Cell membrane	Outer covering of cells that regulates what can enter or leave
Cytoplasm	The watery substance found inside cells where all the chemical reactions of the cell take place
Nucleus	Controls all the activities of a cell and contains the genetic material
Chloroplast	Structure found in green plant cells that contains the pigment **chlorophyll** and where **photosynthesis** takes place
Vacuole	A membrane-bound sac found in plant cells containing a watery solution giving support
Cell wall	Outer covering of plant cells giving support and is made of **cellulose**

Animal and plant cell ultrastructure

Under an **electron microscope**, you can see many more cell structures. Taken together, these are called the **ultrastructure** of a cell. Two examples of additional structures visible under the electron microscope are shown on the diagrams below.

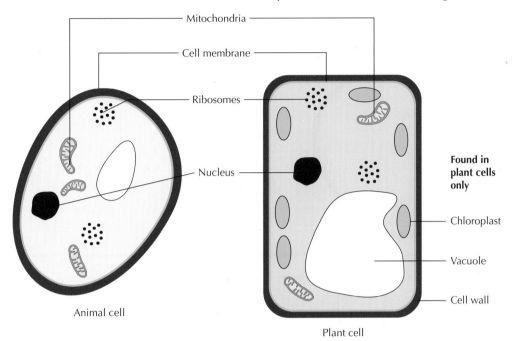

Animal cell

Plant cell

Cell structure	Function
Mitochondrion	Cylindrically-shaped structure found in varying numbers within the cytoplasm of cells that is the site of energy release in aerobic respiration
Ribosome	Small structure that is the site of protein synthesis in a cell

In multicellular organisms, cells can become specialised to perform particular functions. For example, the cells which line the cheek form a continuous layer of cells that are the same size and shape, while cells in a leaf group themselves to form protective coverings or areas where photosynthesis takes place.

Fungal cell ultrastructure

Yeast is an example of a **fungus** that lives as a single-celled organism. Yeast cells are similar to plant cells, having a nucleus, cytoplasm, cell membrane, cell wall, vacuole, ribosomes and mitochondria, but they don't possess chloroplasts so can't photosynthesise. They have a cell wall made of a chemical called **chitin**. Yeast can feed on dead animals and plants and so is very important in decomposition. Some yeasts are used in the manufacture of bread and alcohol.

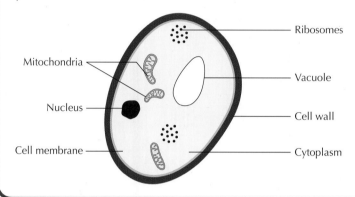

Bacterial cell ultrastructure

Bacteria are single-celled organisms that are usually very small. They share some features with other cells, having a cell wall, cytoplasm, cell membrane and ribosomes, but are also very different in having no nucleus or cell structures such as mitochondria, chloroplasts or vacuoles. In addition to their main genetic material, which is a large circular **chromosome**, they also possess smaller rings of genetic material called **plasmids**. These can reproduce independently of the main genetic material and can also pass between bacteria.

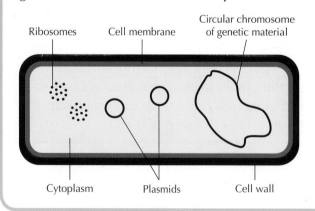

TOP TIP

Make sure you know all the different parts of the cells mentioned and which are present/absent in each cell.

Measuring cell size

Since cells are so small, a special unit of measurement is used. This is called the **micron** (or micrometre) and is often indicated by the symbol μm:

$$1 \text{ μm} = 0.001 \text{ mm}$$
$$1 \text{ mm} = 1000 \text{ μm}$$

If a single-celled animal was 1·5 mm long and 0·5 mm wide, its size would be expressed as 1500 μm by 500 μm.

A human red blood cell is only 8 μm in diameter, equivalent to 0·008 mm.

The table below shows the relative sizes of some structures.

Cell/cell structure	Approximate length/diameter μm
Virus	1
Bacterium	3
Mitochondrion	4
Cheek cell nucleus	5
Red blood cell	8
Sperm	60
Egg cell	130

TOP TIP

You must be able to move between these different units so make sure you practise converting one to the other and have an awareness of the relative sizes of cells.

Quick Test

1. How is the cell wall of a plant cell different from that of a yeast cell?
2. Name two cell structures that cannot be seen with a light microscope.
3. What features do yeast and plant cells have in common?

Transport across cell membranes

Cell membrane

The cell membrane is the structure across which substances must pass if they are to enter or leave a cell. However, the membrane is selective about what can/can't pass across; it is termed **selectively permeable**. Small molecules, such as carbon dioxide, oxygen and water, can pass across easily but larger molecules, such as proteins, cannot.

The structure of the membrane is responsible for these properties and it consists of a layer of two different molecules: proteins and **lipids** arranged as shown below:

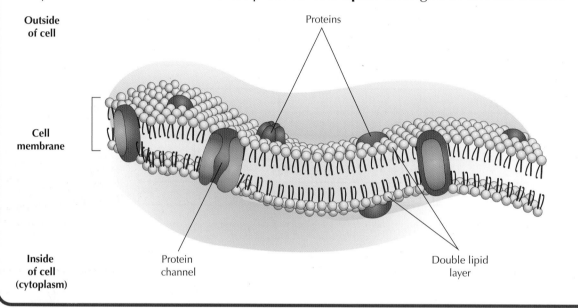

- Outside of cell
- Proteins
- Cell membrane
- Inside of cell (cytoplasm)
- Protein channel
- Double lipid layer

Passive transport and concentration gradient

When materials such as gases, liquids or dissolved substances, move from an area of high concentration to an area of low concentration (that is, down a **concentration gradient**) and no energy is involved, the process is called **passive transport** or **diffusion**. The net movement of such materials will stop once the concentration gradient has been equalised.

Diffusion allows living cells to move many different substances in and out of cells and is a

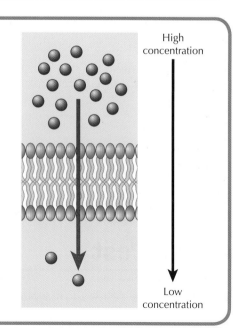

High concentration

Low concentration

vital means for the exchange of important substances between the inside and outside of cells. Here are some examples in an animal cell:

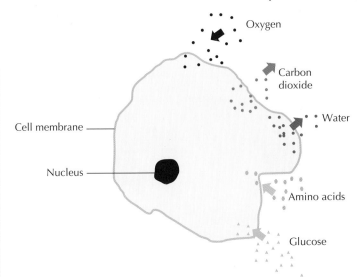

The actual 'direction' of the concentration gradient is dependent on a number of factors. For example, in the lungs the oxygen gradient is from high oxygen concentration outside the cell to low oxygen concentration inside. This gradient will be reversed for cells elsewhere in the body.

TOP TIP

Be able to give examples of diffusion in and out of animal and plant cells in different situations.

Osmosis

A particular example of diffusion is the movement of water molecules from an area of high water concentration to an area of lower water concentration across a selectively permeable membrane. This is called **osmosis**.

In the example below, the sugar molecules do not move so easily or quickly as the water molecules and so there is a change in the volume of solution on either side of the selectively permeable membrane after a time.

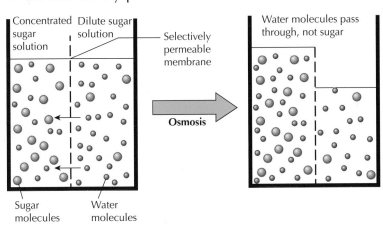

TOP TIP

Remember that osmosis is a special case of diffusion involving the movement of water across a selectively permeable membrane.

The movement of water by osmosis is important for both plant and animal cells. For example, fresh water fish constantly take in water by osmosis across their gills, which act like selectively permeable membranes. In single-celled organisms, water moves across their cell membranes by osmosis. Cells in an animal's body behave similarly.

Cell membrane

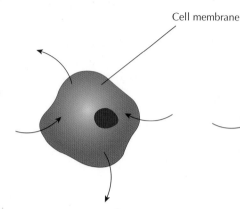

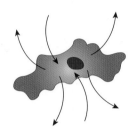

When the water concentration is the same outside and inside there is no net movement of water

When the water concentration is higher outside than inside water moves in and the cell bursts releasing its contents

When the water concentration is higher inside than outside water moves out and the cell shrivels up

Osmosis affects plant and animal cells differently because plant cells have a cell wall. When plant cells swell up due to the intake of water by osmosis, they are termed **turgid**; when they lose water by osmosis, they become **plasmolysed**.

Water

Cell wall

Cell membrane

Vacuole

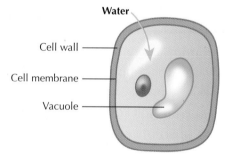

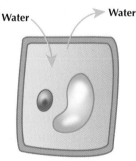

Water

Water

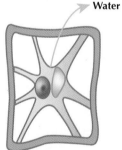

Water

High water concentration outside cell and water moves in by osmosis causing cell to become turgid

Water concentrations inside and outside are the same so no net movement of water

High water concentration inside the cell so water moves out by osmosis causing the cell be become plasmolysed

Active transport

Sometimes diffusion and osmosis are not sufficiently quick or effective for moving substances in and out of cells. For example, the cells in plant roots need to take in nutrients, such as mineral ions, from the soil, where they are in low concentration, into the cells, where they are usually in high concentration. This is therefore against the concentration gradient. Similarly, glucose is moved out of the gut into the bloodstream against a concentration gradient. This type of movement is energy-demanding and is therefore called **active transport**.

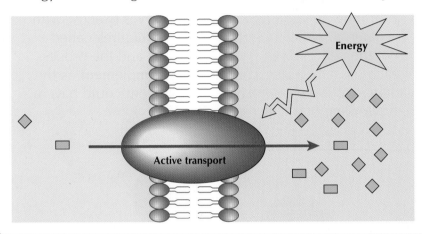

Quick Test

1. Why is the cell membrane described as 'selectively permeable?'
2. State three substances that can enter a cell by diffusion.
3. Give two ways in which active transport differs from diffusion.

Producing new cells

Introduction

TOP TIP

Make sure you understand why mitosis must maintain the number of chromosomes in each daughter cell.

Whenever an organism grows, or if repair or replacement of damaged or worn-out cells is required, new cells are needed. This process is under the control of the cell nucleus. Since the cell's genetic instructions are stored in the nucleus, it is essential that the process of forming new 'daughter' cells preserves exactly, with no loss or gain, this genetic material, which is in the form of structures called **chromosomes**. The division of the cell nucleus is called **mitosis** and the process ensures that the new cells each have the same **chromosome complement** as the original 'parent' cell. Any change to the chromosome complement could have a serious impact on the proper working of a cell.

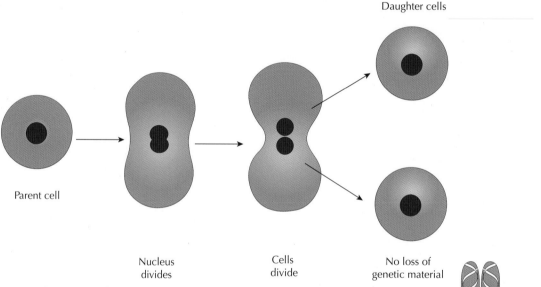

Daughter cells

Parent cell

Nucleus divides

Cells divide

No loss of genetic material

The chromosomes in a cell are not usually visible until the cell is about to divide by mitosis, when they become short and thick and easily seen under the microscope. Each chromosome is then apparent as two identical strands called **chromatids**, which are held together by a structure called the **centromere**. During mitosis, fibres, which make up a **spindle**, attach to these centromeres and move the chromosomes around.

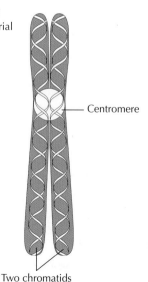

Centromere

Two chromatids

Process of mitosis

The diagram shows a complete set of the 46 human chromosomes arranged in 23 pairs. Other species of living things contain different numbers of chromosomes. The total number of chromosomes in a cell is called the **diploid number**; for humans it is 46, for a gorilla 48 and a pig 38.

Mitosis ensures that every daughter cell gets exactly the same chromosomes as its parent cell. While this takes place continuously, it is easier to study if considered in stages.

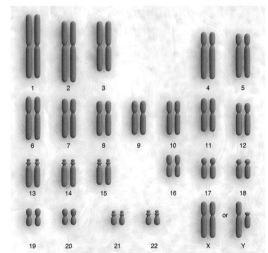

TOP TIP

Make sure you understand the distinction between chromosome and chromatid.

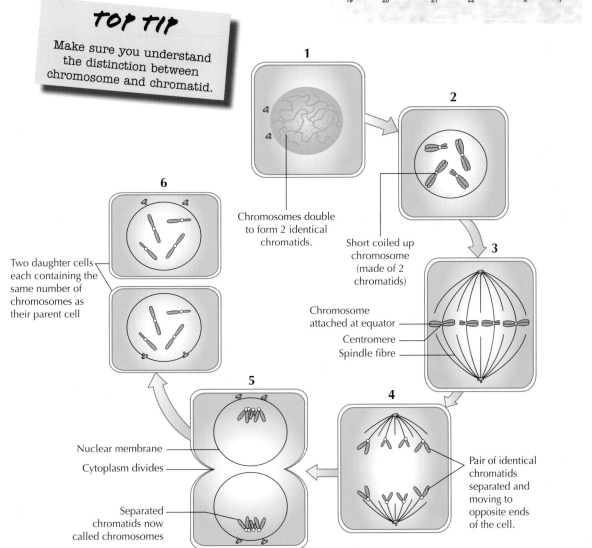

1 Chromosomes double to form 2 identical chromatids.

2 Short coiled up chromosome (made of 2 chromatids)

3 Chromosome attached at equator
Centromere
Spindle fibre

4 Pair of identical chromatids separated and moving to opposite ends of the cell.

5 Nuclear membrane
Cytoplasm divides
Separated chromatids now called chromosomes

6 Two daughter cells each containing the same number of chromosomes as their parent cell

Cell culture

To grow cells under carefully controlled laboratory conditions, three particularly important **cell culture** techniques have been developed:

1. **enzymes** are used to break down the contact between cells to isolate them from each other and allow them to be grown separately

2. use of drugs called **antibiotics** allows the cells to grow **aseptically**, that is, without contamination

3. appropriate media have been produced to a very high standard and meet the demands of the growing cells very precisely.

TOP TIP

Make sure you know what techniques are used to prevent contamination of cultures.

In order to grow cells in this way, strict procedures are followed in the laboratory to ensure asepsis. In addition, a number of factors must be controlled: oxygen and nutrient availability, pH and temperature, which usually rely on automated systems.

The application of cell culture is very extensive. For example, plants can easily be grown in glass tubes or on plates by removing samples of cells from different parts of the adult plant.

Cells can be grown in different types of growth media. These include solid **agar** and liquid broth.

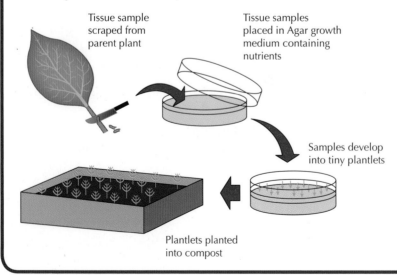

Tissue sample scraped from parent plant

Tissue samples placed in Agar growth medium containing nutrients

Samples develop into tiny plantlets

Plantlets planted into compost

The use of cell culture means that whole, live animals are hardly used in research at all now.

When large numbers of cells need to be grown in the laboratory, they are sometimes introduced into a **fermenter**, allowing their rapid production under carefully controlled conditions.

Quick Test

1. The process of mitosis ensures that the daughter cells all receive the same diploid number of chromosomes. Why is this important?

2. What is the diploid number of the cell shown in the diagram?

3. Which structure holds chromatids together?

DNA and production of proteins

Structure of DNA

The chromosomes in the nucleus of living cells contain a chemical called **deoxyribonucleic acid**, commonly shortened to **DNA**. Each molecule of DNA is made up of two strands twisted around each other to form a coiled, ladder-like shape called a **double helix**.

Each strand is, in turn, composed of many repeating building-blocks called **nucleotides**. A DNA nucleotide consists of 5-carbon sugar called **deoxyribose**, a phosphate grouping and one of four nitrogen-containing chemicals, **adenine**, **thymine**, **guanine** and **adenine**, collectively called **bases**.

Each of the two strands is held together by weak links called **hydrogen bonds** between the bases, which are in the middle of the double helix. The phosphate and deoxyribose form the backbone of the double helix. The bases are linked together in specific or **complementary** pairings.

Adenine always pairs with thymine, while cytosine always pairs with guanine. The sequence of the bases is responsible for the types of protein made in cells.

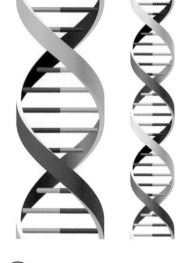

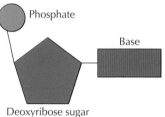

Phosphate

Base

Deoxyribose sugar

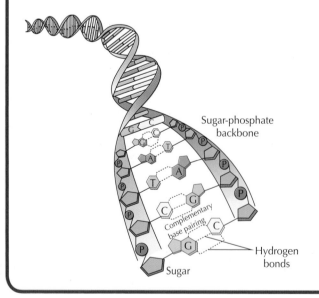

Sugar-phosphate backbone

Complementary base pairing

Hydrogen bonds

Sugar

TOP TIP

The differences that exist between living things are due to the differences in the sequence of the bases in their nucleic acids.

DNA and protein

All the reactions that go on inside a cell are controlled by **enzymes**. Enzymes are made of proteins built up from units called **amino acids**.

Amino acids

Join up in particular order to form protein

Enzymes act as biological **catalysts** and are responsible for the function, growth and development of cells and whole organisms. Enzyme production is controlled by DNA. The actual structures that join up the amino acids in a particular order, determined by the base sequence of the DNA, to form proteins in cells, are the ribosomes found in the cytoplasm. The ribosomes and DNA are 'linked' by a special carrier molecule called **messenger ribonucleic acid** or **mRNA** for short.

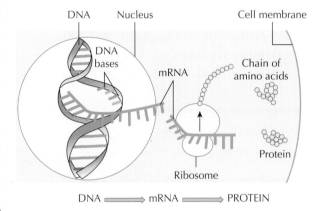

DNA ⟹ mRNA ⟹ PROTEIN

Quick Test

1. Which three chemicals make up one nucleotide?

2. Give the correct complementary pairing of adenine (A), thymine (T), cytosine (C) and guanine (G).

3. State two properties of enzymes.

Proteins and enzymes

Introduction

Many other important chemicals are made up of proteins. The variety of structures and functions of proteins arise from the different sequence of the amino acids present.

Proteins	Function
Enzymes	Catalyse chemical reactions in a cell
Hormones	Chemicals that act as messengers and affect how living things develop and behave
Antibodies	Large molecules that help defend against infections
Haemoglobin	Transports oxygen in the bloodstream
Collagen	Forms part of rigid bone structure

Proteins, such as collagen, that form parts of a cell or give it support and rigidity, are termed **structural**. Another example of a structural protein is **keratin**, which is found in the skin and gives it toughness. Keratin is also the major protein that makes up hair and nails.

TOP TIP

Remember, it is the sequence of the bases in the DNA that determines protein structure and function.

Enzymes

Enzymes are the biological catalysts made by living cells that speed up reactions without being changed themselves. Each enzyme is specific for the chemical on which it acts, called the **substrate**. This means that an enzyme will react with only one particular substrate. The resultant chemicals are called the products. The area where the enzyme and substrate meet is called the **active site**, which is complementary in shape to the substrate.

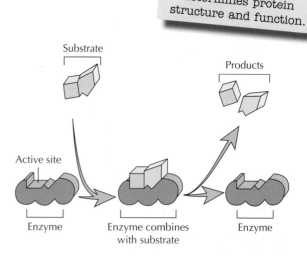

Substrate

Products

Active site

Enzyme

Enzyme combines with substrate

Enzyme

Factors affecting enzyme activity

Two important factors that affect enzyme activity are pH and temperature. This is because enzymes are made of proteins, which are sensitive to changes in the pH and temperature of their surroundings. Each enzyme has a particular pH and temperature at which it works best called the **optimum**.

Most enzymes work best at a pH near neutral (7) but others, such as those in the stomach, work best in acidic conditions; those found in the liver and bone, work best in alkaline conditions.

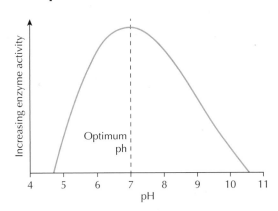

Enzymes are also very sensitive to changes in temperature, working best at an optimum determined by the type of organism in which the enzyme-catalysed reaction is taking place. In humans with a body temperature of about 37°C, the optimum temperature for enzyme function is also very close to 37°C.

When a factor, such as pH or temperature, goes much above or below the optimum, enzyme function slows down. If the change in structure (and hence function) is irreversible, the enzyme is said to be **denatured** and the active site is no longer able to bind with its specific substrate.

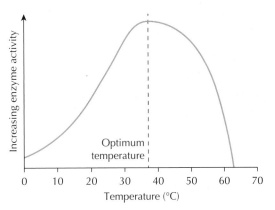

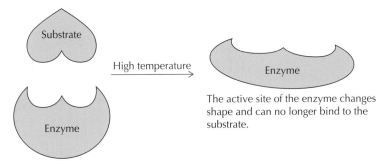

The active site of the enzyme changes shape and can no longer bind to the substrate.

Quick Test

1. Why is the sequence of amino acids in a protein so important?
2. Why is one enzyme that breaks down starch not effective in breaking down protein?
3. Give one possible explanation why storing food in a fridge extends its shelf-life.

Genetic engineering

Genetic engineering

It is now possible artificially to transfer specific parts of a cell's genetic material, called **genes**, from one **species** to an entirely different species. These techniques come under the general heading of **genetic engineering**. This process enables the **genetically modified** cell or organism to make or do something it did not before. For example, the following sequence is used to **transform** a bacterial cell to make the human hormone **insulin**.

Gene on human chromosome for producing human insulin is identified

Insulin producing gene is extracted

Bacterial plasmid is extracted and opened

Gene is inserted into the bacterial plasmid

Plasmid is put back into original bacterium

Bacterium allowed to reproduce

Multiple copies of the plasmids are made

Bacteria produce insulin, which is harvested

TOP TIP

Make sure you know the sequence involved in genetically modifying a cell and the function of a plasmid as a vector.

TOP TIP

You need to be able to understand information presented in different ways, sometimes in text form, sometimes a diagram etc.

Notice that the bacterial plasmid is acting as a 'carrier' or **vector** to transport the human gene into the bacterial cell.

The diagram below shows the same process.

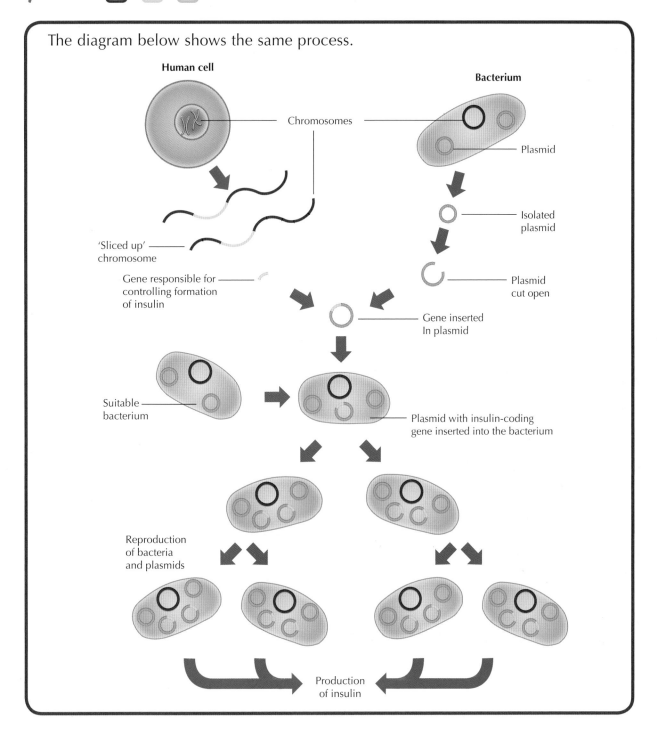

Human cell

Bacterium

Chromosomes

Plasmid

'Sliced up' chromosome

Isolated plasmid

Gene responsible for controlling formation of insulin

Plasmid cut open

Gene inserted In plasmid

Suitable bacterium

Plasmid with insulin-coding gene inserted into the bacterium

Reproduction of bacteria and plasmids

Production of insulin

Quick Test

1. What is a 'gene'?
2. Give two reasons why people might be concerned about the application of genetic engineering to produce genetically modified (GM) foods.
3. Give one example of a vector that can be used in genetic engineering.

Photosynthesis

Introduction

One of the most fundamental differences between animals and plants is how they obtain their food. Whereas animals need to have their food 'ready-made' in the form of other animals or plants, plants use the energy of the sun to produce their own food in the form of the **carbohydrate**, **glucose** (a type of sugar). This process is called photosynthesis and takes place in the chloroplasts of green plant cells. The green chlorophyll in the chloroplasts traps the light energy. Oxygen is released during photosynthesis, which can be summarised by the following word equation:

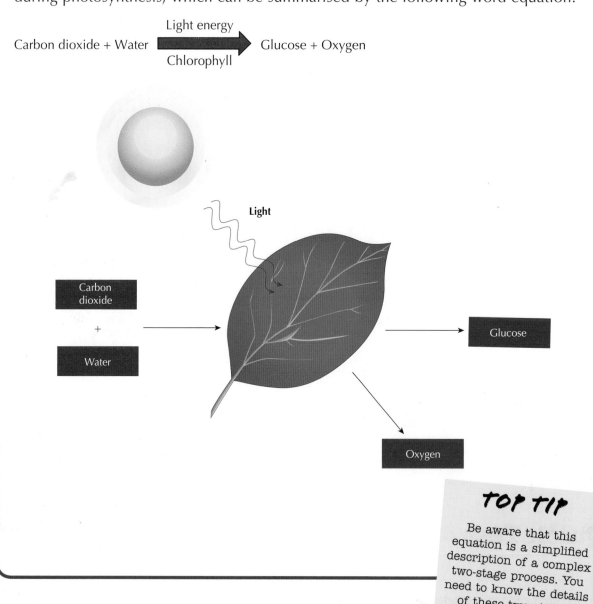

Carbon dioxide + Water $\xrightarrow[\text{Chlorophyll}]{\text{Light energy}}$ Glucose + Oxygen

TOP TIP

Be aware that this equation is a simplified description of a complex two-stage process. You need to know the details of these two stages.

Chemistry of photosynthesis

Photosynthesis has two stages, both consisting of many enzyme-controlled reactions. The first stage needs light energy, which is trapped by chlorophyll and used to produce ATP from **adenosine diphosphate (ADP)** and phosphate. Water, taken in by the roots of the plant, is split into hydrogen and oxygen using the energy of sunlight. The hydrogen is used in the second stage, which does not need light, while the oxygen diffuses out of the cell. In the second stage, the hydrogen combines with carbon dioxide to form glucose and the energy to drive this comes from ATP. This is called **carbon fixation**.

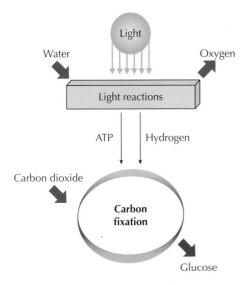

The glucose produced by photosynthesis can be used in many different ways by the plant. For example, it can be converted into plant products such as **starch** or cellulose. When light is not available, the plant still needs energy and it obtains this by breaking down the glucose. Glucose can also be converted into **fats** and **oils** as well as **proteins**.

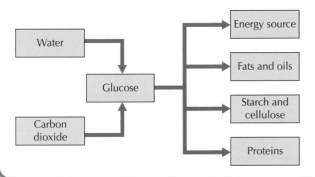

TOP TIP

Photosynthesis is vital for life on Earth because it produces food and oxygen for animals.

Limiting factors

Since cell growth is closely linked to how fast photosynthesis takes place, anything that affects this process will in turn speed up or slow down the growth of the plant. One way of measuring the rate of photosynthesis is to measure the volume of oxygen produced in a fixed time by an aquatic plant. It is also possible to use the increase in the dry mass of a plant or volume of carbon dioxide taken in within a fixed time.

Three important factors will affect the rate of photosynthesis:

1. temperature

2. light intensity

3. carbon dioxide concentration.

At any one time, only one factor limits the rate of photosynthesis; this is therefore called the **limiting factor**.

As the light intensity increases from point A to B, the rate of photosynthesis increases until it starts to level off and then stays constant at point C. At this value of light intensity some other limiting factor, such as temperature or carbon dioxide concentration, is preventing an increase in the rate of photosynthesis.

As the concentration of carbon dioxide increases, the rate of photosynthesis increases but eventually levels off as some other limiting factor, such as light intensity or temperature, is preventing an increase in the rate of photosynthesis.

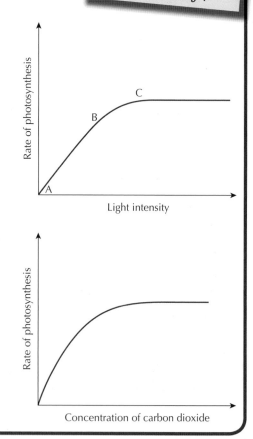

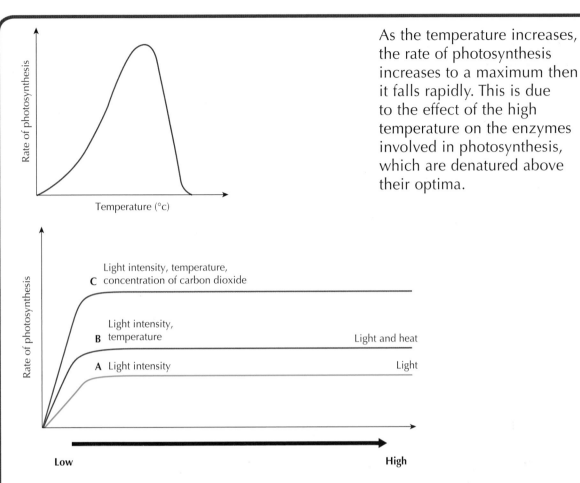

As the temperature increases, the rate of photosynthesis increases to a maximum then it falls rapidly. This is due to the effect of the high temperature on the enzymes involved in photosynthesis, which are denatured above their optima.

The above graph illustrates these three limiting factors acting together. The green line shows that more light intensity increases the rate of photosynthesis until point A when an increase in light intensity has no further effect. Another factor is limiting the rate of photosynthesis. The red line shows the effect of increasing temperature along with light intensity. A new, higher rate of photosynthesis is obtained but this also reaches a maximum at point B, when no further increase in light intensity or temperature increases the rate of photosynthesis. The blue line shows the effect of increasing the concentration of carbon dioxide as well as light intensity and temperature. Again, a new higher rate of photosynthesis is obtained that reaches a maximum at point C when no further increase in any of these three limiting factors will increase the rate of photosynthesis.

TOP TIP

This type of presentation with more than one limiting factor is often asked in examinations.

Quick Test

1.   What is meant by the term 'carbon fixation'?

2.   Give two possible uses for the glucose made in photosynthesis.

3.   What is meant by a 'limiting factor'?

Respiration

Introduction

Glucose is an energy-rich molecule but this stored energy has to be released in a controlled way to prevent damage to cells. To ensure the safe release of this energy, a large number of small steps is used. Each step is under the control of an enzyme; collectively, these steps are called **respiration**.

ATP and respiration

> **TOP TIP**
>
> ATP is not an energy store but transfers energy.

The energy released from glucose is not used directly by living cells but is used to synthesise ATP from ADP and phosphate. ATP is a universally found chemical in plant and animals cells as the source of immediate energy.

This ATP can be broken down directly to drive any reaction that needs energy and then be reformed as needed from ADP and phosphate using energy from the breakdown of more glucose:

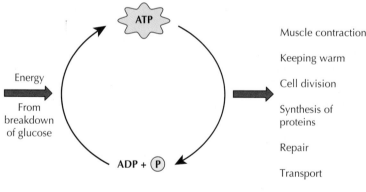

Muscle contraction

Keeping warm

Cell division

Synthesis of proteins

Repair

Transport

Nerve transmission

> **TOP TIP**
>
> Different cells in an animal or plant have different energy demands. Make sure you can name examples from each that require a lot of energy to function.

In animals, such as humans, that keep their body temperature constant at around 37°C, the heat is supplied by cells as they respire glucose. It is no accident their enzymes work best at this temperature!

Aerobic respiration

The breakdown of glucose normally takes place in the presence of oxygen and for this reason is termed **aerobic**. This form of respiration results in the complete breakdown of the glucose to form carbon dioxide and water as well as ATP.

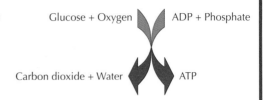

Glucose + Oxygen   ADP + Phosphate

Carbon dioxide + Water   ATP

This process is a series of steps, each catalysed by its own specific enzyme. The first stage of aerobic respiration takes place in the cell cytoplasm and results in the production of a 3-C molecule called **pyruvate** and 2 molecules of ATP. The pyruvate is then further broken down in the mitochondria of the cell to produce carbon dioxide, water and ATP. Since the glucose is completely broken down in aerobic respiration, this is a very efficient process. It yields, in total, 38 molecules of ATP for every 1 molecule of glucose respired.

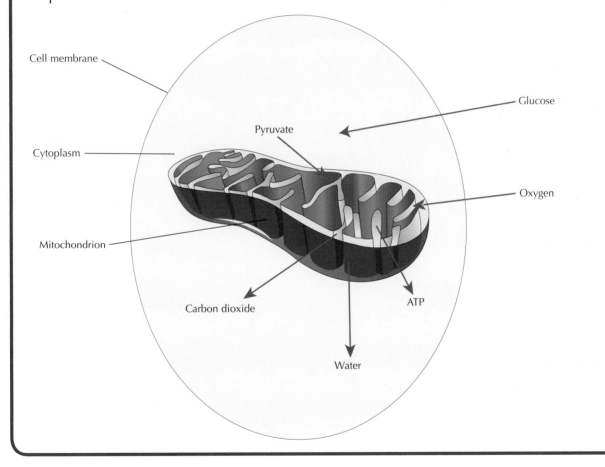

Respiration without oxygen in animals

Sometimes, for short periods only, animals can respire without oxygen. This is termed **anaerobic respiration**. For example, during strenuous exercise, it might not be possible to meet the excessive oxygen demand by working muscles, which use up all the available oxygen. In this situation, glucose cannot be completely respired. The pyruvate is instead converted to **lactic acid**.

If lactic acid accumulates in the bloodstream, it causes cramp and stops the muscles working efficiently. Anaerobic respiration is not a very efficient process for several reasons:

1. glucose is only partly broken down

2. lactic acid still contains a lot of energy

3. only 2 molecules of ATP are produced.

Exercising muscle

↓

Glucose

↓ → ATP

Pyruvic acid

↓

Lactic acid → Into blood

Respiration without oxygen in plant and fungal cells

In some situations, cells can respire anaerobically for periods of time, but not indefinitely. For example, if plant roots get flooded with water and deprived of oxygen, they will switch to anaerobic respiration until oxygen becomes available. The pyruvate is converted into an alcohol called **ethanol** and carbon dioxide.

Yeast cells can break down glucose in the absence of oxygen. This is called **fermentation**.

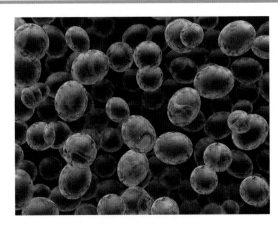

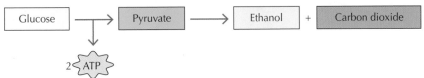

Aerobic respiration	Anaerobic respiration/fermentation
Needs oxygen	Does not need oxygen
Efficient in producing 38 ATP molecules for every 1 molecule of glucose respired	Inefficient in producing only 2 ATP molecules for every 1 molecule of glucose respired
Can carry on indefinitely	Can only last relatively short periods of time
Glucose completely broken down	Glucose not completely broken down
End-products are carbon dioxide and water	End-products are lactic acid in animal cells and ethanol and carbon dioxide in plant and yeast cells
Starts in the cytoplasm and is completed in the mitochondria	Takes place only in the cytoplasm

Quick Test

1. Why does respiration take place in many small steps?
2. What is the common simple sugar that is used as a substrate for respiration?
3. Copy and complete the following word equation for aerobic respiration:

   + oxygen ⟶ carbon dioxide +   +

End of Unit Questions

Section A

1. The diagram below shows a human cell viewed under an electron microscope.

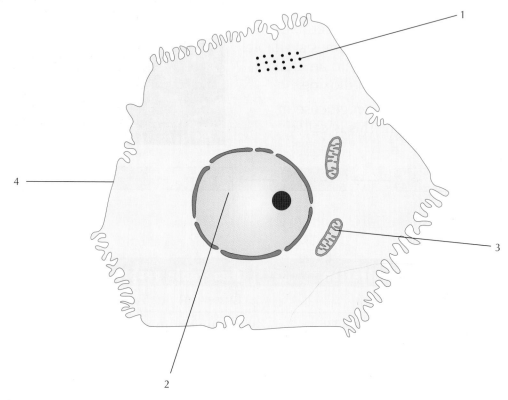

Which of the following correctly identifies structures 1, 2, 3 and 4?

	1	2	3	4
A	Mitochondrion	Cell membrane	Nucleus	Ribosomes
B	Cell membrane	Mitochondrion	Ribosomes	Nucleus
C	Nucleus	Cell membrane	Ribosomes	Mitochondrion
D	Ribosomes	Nucleus	Mitochondrion	Cell membrane

2. If a mitochondrion appears to be 12 mm under a magnification of × 12 000, what is its size in μm?

   A 0·5

   B 1·0

   C 1·5

   D 2·0

3. A piece of plant material was weighed and then placed in strong sugar
   solution for 45 minutes then in pure water for 45 minutes. It was removed,
   dried and reweighed after each immersion.

   Which of the following is very likely to be the readings obtained?

	Initial mass (g)	After 45 mins in strong sugar (g)	After 45 mins in water (g)
A	10	12	10
B	8	7	6
C	12	10	14
D	9	8	7

4. When a yeast cell breaks down one molecule of glucose during fermentation,
   how many ATP molecules are gained?

   A 1

   B 2

   C 36

   D 38

5. The following diagram shows part of the DNA molecule.

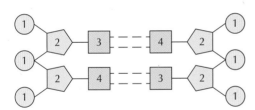

   If 4 represents the base adenine, which of the following correctly identifies the
   other numbered structures?

	Sugar	Phosphate	Thymine
A	1	2	3
B	2	3	1
C	3	1	2
D	2	1	3

Section B

1. The following graph shows the change in the rate of an enzyme-catalysed reaction with increasing temperature. The rate is measured in 'units'.

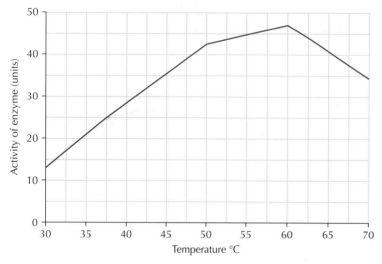

    (a) What is the optimum temperature for this enzyme?   [1]

    (b) What is the percentage increase in the activity of the enzyme when the temperature is increased from 37·5°C to 45°C ?   [1]

    (c) (i) Is this enzyme likely to be from an animal?   [1]

        (ii) Explain your answer.   [2]

2. The following diagram shows a cell undergoing division by mitosis.

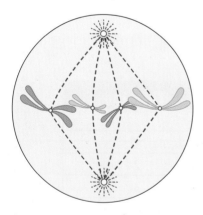

    (a) How many chromosomes are present?   [1]

    (b) How many sets of chromosomes are present?   [1]

    (c) On the diagram, label one chromatid using the letter C.   [1]

3. (a) The diagram below shows a plant cell after immersion in three different solutions.

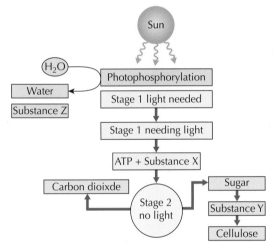

A   B   C

    (i) What term is used to describe the condition of cell A? [1]

    (ii) In which cell was the initial water concentration inside lower than that outside? [1]

(b) Explain why a red blood cell bursts after being placed in pure water. [2]

4. (a) The diagram below shows parts of a process that takes place in plants.

    (i) What term is used to describe this process? [1]

    (ii) Identify each of the substances labelled X, Y and Z. [1]

(b) What substance in a plant traps the light energy needed for this process? [1]

5. A student's breathing rate was measured at rest, after jogging for 20, 40 and 60 seconds. The following data were obtained.

Breathing measured	Breathing rate (breaths/per minute)
At rest	15
After jogging for 20 seconds	20
After jogging for 40 seconds	30
After jogging for 60 seconds	40

(a) Plot these results as a **bar chart**. [3]

(b) What is the percentage increase in the breathing rate from at rest to after jogging for 60 seconds? [1]

(c) Express, as a **simple whole number** ratio, the breathing rates at each of the four measured periods. [1]

Cells, tissues and organs

Specialisation of cells

While cells of different living things share many features in common, they show great variation in their size, shape and function. In more complex, **multicellular** organisms, cells of similar size, shape and function often group together to form **tissues**.

Cells that form tissues are usually **specialised** so that different jobs can be done more effectively. Tissues, in turn, are grouped to form **organs**.

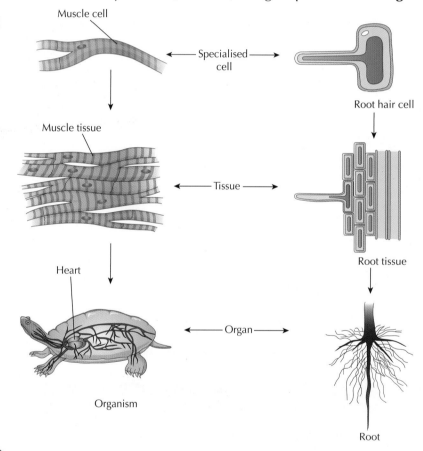

Muscle cell

←—— Specialised ——→
cell

Root hair cell

Muscle tissue

←——— Tissue ———→

Root tissue

Heart

←——— Organ ———→

Root

Organism

Quick Test

1.	What term describes an organism made up of many cells?
2.	What general term describes a group of cells that are all the same size and shape and perform a similar function?
3.	The leaf of a plant carries out photosynthesis. It consists of groups of cells that trap sunlight energy, transport water, allow gas exchange and protect the leaf. What general term describes a leaf as a collection of these different groups?

Stem cells and meristems

Stem cells in animals

It has been estimated that in one day, you will shed about a million skin cells! These have to be constantly replaced. This requires a supply of new cells as well as maintaining the original population of cells which gives rise to the new skin cells. The original population is made up of cells that are not yet committed but can form specialised skin cells. These uncommitted cells are called **stem cells** and are extremely important in animals. They have three important features:

1. are not yet committed to be a particular type of cell

2. can divide repeatedly without limit during an animal's lifetime

3. divide to form two daughter cells, each of which may remain a stem cell or become another type of specialised cell.

TOP TIP

Stem cells are found in many different places in an animal's body such as bone marrow, teeth, lungs, heart and brain.

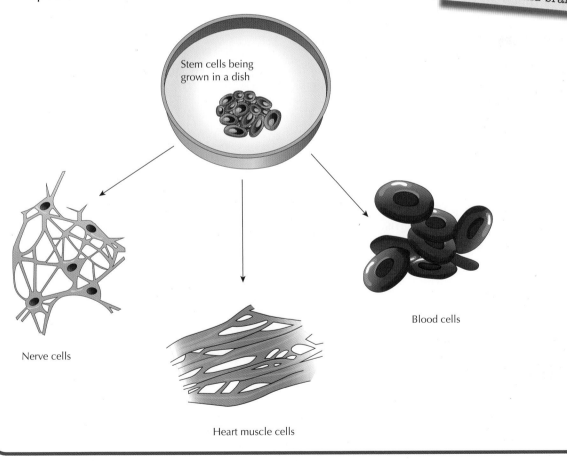

Stem cells being grown in a dish

Nerve cells

Heart muscle cells

Blood cells

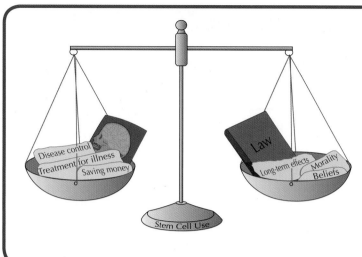

Adult stem cells function to repair and replace damaged or worn out cells in the tissues where they are found. Research into the uses of stem cells involves looking at ways to grow them in large numbers, then making them produce specific types of cells to treat injuries or diseases. Their use is not without some ethical issues, particularly in relation to the source of the stem cells.

Meristems in plants

While growth in an animal takes place all over its body, growth in plants is confined to particular areas called **meristems**. In meristems, non-specialised cells are produced that are capable of active cell division to form more unspecialised cells, as well as ones that perform particular jobs. Meristems consist of relatively small cells that can grow and mature to form new plant tissues. Meristems found at the tips of growing roots and shoots are termed **apical;** those found towards the outside of roots and stems are called **lateral**. Activity of apical meristems results in

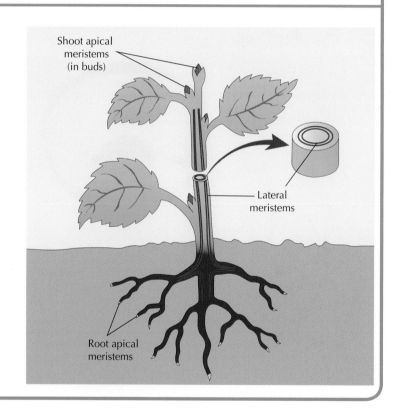

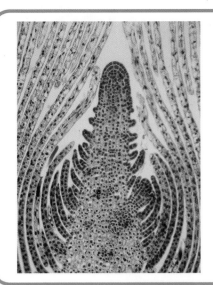

an increase in the length of a root or shoot while activity in lateral meristems results in an increase in the width of a root or shoot.

The image on the left shows a light micrograph of an apical meristem at the end of a plant bud.

Quick Test

1. State 3 features of a stem cell.
2. Which of the following statements is NOT true?
    a) Stem cells cannot grow in large numbers.
    b) Growth takes place all over the body of a plant.
    c) Meristems can produce an increase in the width of a tree.
    d) During the lifetime of an animal, stem cells can divide repeatedly.
3. How does an apical meristem differ from a lateral meristem?

Control and communication

Structure and function of the central nervous system

To preserve and maintain life, a multicellular animal requires an efficient means of detecting changes in its environment such as sound, temperature increase or decrease, light intensity, etc. Such changes are called stimuli. The animal must then be able to react to those stimuli in an appropriate way.

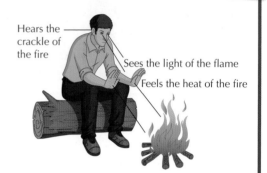

Hears the crackle of the fire

Sees the light of the flame

Feels the heat of the fire

Additionally, the animal must be able to monitor its 'internal environment' to control the rates of heartbeat and breathing, and check for constancy in the pH of the blood, levels of nutrients, etc. The **nervous system** is responsible for this control.

All over an animal's body there are special cells or groups of cells that can detect specific stimuli. These **sensory receptors** send information about what is happening externally as well as internally to the **central nervous system (CNS)**. The central nervous system consists of the **brain** and **spinal cord**. The spinal cord is protected by a series of bones that make up a tube called the **spinal column**.

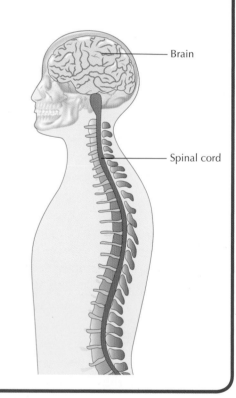

Brain

Spinal cord

The main functions of the nervous system in an animal's body are to:

- send information to all parts
- receive information from all parts
- make sense of the information received
- co-ordinate the workings of internal organs
- respond to stimuli in the external environment.

The brain

This remarkable organ consists of three important structures: **cerebrum** (divided into two halves called the **cerebral hemispheres**), **cerebellum** and **medulla**. Each performs particular functions.

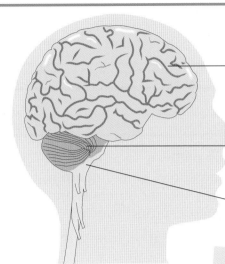

Cerebrum controls all higher activities such as memory, emotions, sensations, concious decisions, processing information and intelligence

Cerebellum controls balance and co-ordinates muscles involved in precise and accurate movements

Medulla controls activities that the animal is not conciously aware of, such as breathing, digestion and heartbeat

TOP TIP

Make sure you can label a diagram of the brain and know what the functions of each of the three important parts are.

Reflex action

Multicellular animals inherit the ability to respond quickly and without thinking to some stimuli, particularly ones that might be harmful. For example, the simple act of a dog blinking its eyes is an unconscious mechanism for constantly cleaning and keeping the surface of the eye moist and thereby inhibiting infection. Such unconscious actions are called **reflexes**. Sneezing, coughing, blinking, withdrawing from a hot or sharp object are all examples of reflexes. In animals with short lifespans, reflexes save valuable time and energy as they don't need to be learned and help the animal survive because it can focus on other immediate aspects of its environment.

TOP TIP

There are many examples of reflexes that help an animal survive. Make sure you know a number of these and how they increase the chances of survival.

In general, reflexes:

- give rise to a 'pre-programmed' type of response to a given stimulus
- are usually not under conscious control though, sometimes, they can be influenced by a voluntary input

- give rise to very rapid responses to appropriate stimuli
- generally cannot be stopped once they have started
- often do not involve the brain in any way
- usually follow very simple pathways involving few nerve cells.

Reflex arc

A **reflex arc** is a very simple pathway for a reflex action and typically involves three special nerve cells, sometimes called **neurons**, acting in series. At either end is a **receptor**, which detects a specific stimulus and an **effector**, which performs some kind of action. The three neurons involved are:

1. **sensory neuron** carrying information from a receptor to a relay neuron

2. **relay neuron** connects a sensory neuron to a motor neuron

3. **motor neuron** carrying information towards an effector which may be a muscle or **gland.**

TOP TIP

Information travels incredibly quickly along nerves as impulses.

Between one neuron and the next is a tiny gap called a **synapse**. When a nerve impulse reaches the end of one neurone, a small quantity of a chemical is released, which diffuses across the gap to the next neuron. This is then stimulated to carry the impulse, rather like a baton being passed from one runner to the next in a relay race.

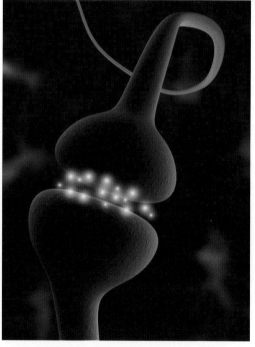

Synapses allow:

- nerve impulses to travel in one direction because the chemical is released from one neuron and travels across the gap to the next neuron but not the other way around
- multiple connections between different neurons to be made
- control of the on-going nerve impulse by altering the type and quantity of chemical released so that the on-going impulse may be strengthened or weakened or prevented entirely.

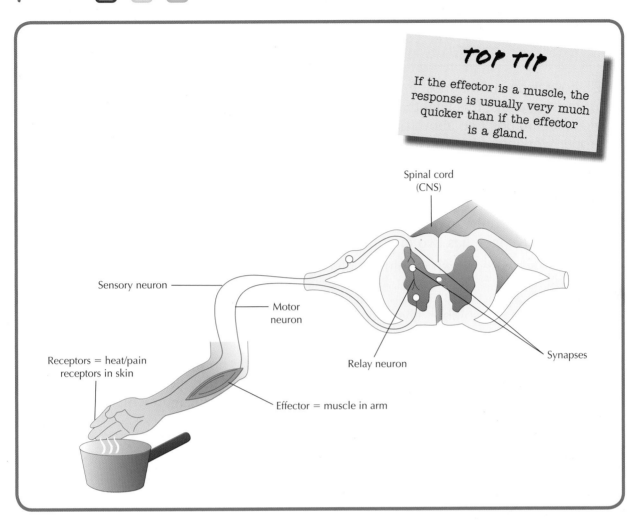

TOP TIP

If the effector is a muscle, the response is usually very much quicker than if the effector is a gland.

Spinal cord (CNS)

Sensory neuron

Motor neuron

Relay neuron

Synapses

Receptors = heat/pain receptors in skin

Effector = muscle in arm

Hormonal control

Sometimes a slower response is required to a stimulus, or the cells affected by that stimulus are located in different parts of an animal's body. In these situations, the **endocrine system** for co-ordination comes into operation. This contains many **endocrine glands**, which release hormones directly into the blood stream. The cells sensitive to the hormones are called **target tissues**. Target cells have special **receptors** on their surface, which means that only those cells are affected by a specific hormone.

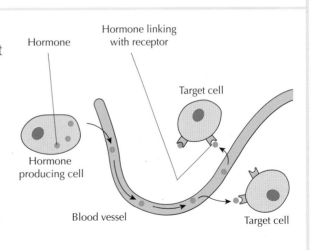

Hormone

Hormone linking with receptor

Target cell

Hormone producing cell

Blood vessel

Target cell

Blood glucose regulation

Glucose is one of the most important sources of energy for most animals. It is vital that the levels of glucose in the bloodstream don't go above or below a critical value or the proper working of body cells is reduced. If this occurs and continues, eventually the whole animal will be affected.

TOP TIP

Glucose is the only source of energy for brain cells.

The source of an animal's glucose is its food but since animals don't eat all the time, they must store glucose until it is needed. After eating, the level of glucose is very high and so the excess is stored in the form of a chemical called **glycogen** in the liver. Glycogen has two important properties:

1. unlike glucose, which is soluble, glycogen is insoluble and so can be easily stored

2. because it is insoluble, glycogen does not cause osmosis to take place as glucose does.

To promote the conversion of glucose to glycogen, the hormone insulin is produced by an endocrine gland called the **pancreas**. When glucose is required, the pancreas is able to produce another hormone called **glucagon** which converts the glycogen back into glucose.

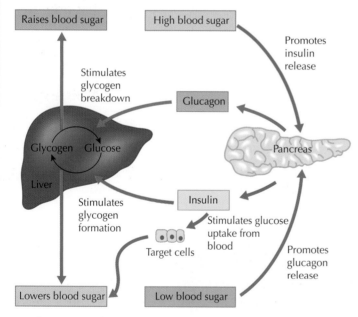

In this way, the level of glucose in the blood is kept at a constant level.

Diabetes

Some people suffer from a condition called **diabetes** which means they are unable to control their blood glucose levels properly. It is essentially a breakdown in communication due to a fault in the mechanism for producing or responding to insulin. This breakdown means the body cannot cope with the high levels of glucose produced after the digestion of a meal and then, later, the levels of glucose fall too low until the next meal.

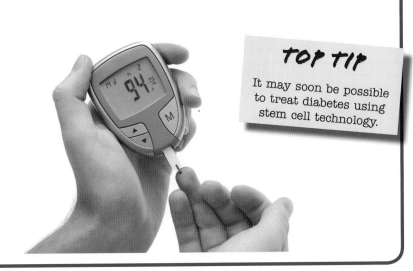

The major symptoms of diabetes include:

- unusual thirst
- tiredness
- loss of weight
- blurred vision
- increased hunger
- appearance of glucose in the urine.

There are now very good treatments to manage diabetes that allow those affected to live normal lives. The major form of treatment consists of daily insulin injections, usually self-administered, along with monitoring of diet and regular exercise.

TOP TIP

It may soon be possible to treat diabetes using stem cell technology.

Quick Test

1.	What two body systems are responsible for control and communication?
2.	What is meant by a 'stimulus'?
3.	Give two reasons why glycogen is such a good storage carbohydrate.

Reproduction

Diploid and haploid cells

The cells that make up the body of a plant or animal contain the diploid number of chromosomes (n). The diploid number in a pigeon is 80 and in rice it is 24. During reproduction, special **sex cells** or **gametes** are formed, which contain half the diploid number. This is called the **haploid number** (2n).

Haploid (n)

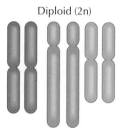
Diploid (2n)

In animals, sex cells are produced in structures called **gonads**. These are usually the **testes** (singular **testis**), which produce **sperm**, and **ovaries**, which produce **eggs** or **ova** (singular **ovum**).

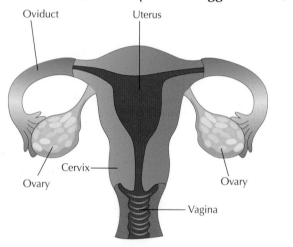
Oviduct, Uterus, Cervix, Ovary, Ovary, Vagina

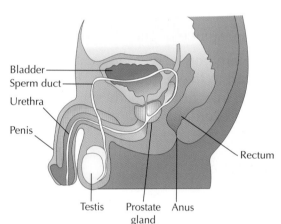
Bladder, Sperm duct, Urethra, Penis, Testis, Prostate gland, Anus, Rectum

Eggs and sperm differ in their structure and function.

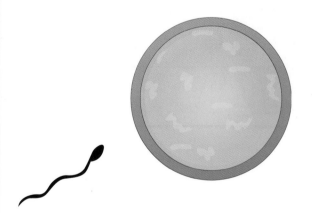

> **TOP TIP**
> Look at other diagrams in different presentations so you are familiar with a frontal and side view of each.

> **TOP TIP**
> Make a table listing the differences in the structure and function of an egg and a sperm.

In flowering plants, the female gametes are within the **ovules** and formed in the ovary. The male gametes are within the **pollen grains** and formed in the **anther**.

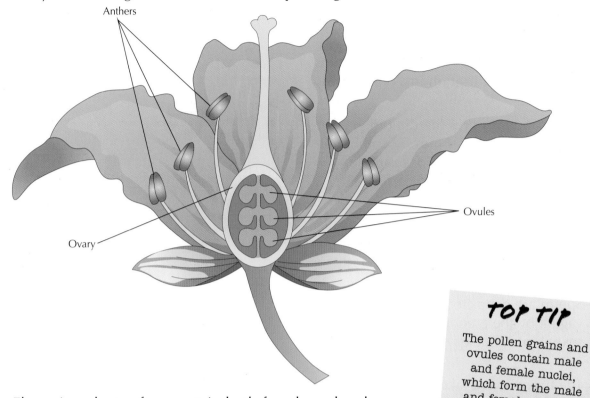

Anthers

Ovules

Ovary

TOP TIP

The pollen grains and ovules contain male and female nuclei, which form the male and female gametes respectively.

Flowering plants often contain both female and male reproductive structures in the same flower.

Gametes in both animals and plants each:

• contain only half the diploid number of chromosomes and therefore only half the genetic material of normal body cells

• are unique combinations of genetic material from the parent organism that produced them.

The way in which gametes are produced in plants and animals allows for unlimited variation in the new organisms formed in subsequent generations. Each parent contributes, randomly, half its genetic material to form a gamete so that the newly formed organism is a unique combination of genes from each parent, giving rise to the variety of different forms of a species.

Fertilisation

For a new individual to form, a male and female gamete must fuse to form a **zygote**. This event is called **fertilisation**. In animals, fertilisation involves sperms and eggs.

Fertilisation restores the diploid number of chromosomes by combining two haploid gametes. For example, in humans, each gamete carries 23 chromosomes (n).

The life cycle of a multicellular organism alternates between a diploid state for the body cells and a haploid state for the gametes.

Sperm are deposited inside the vagina by the erect penis during sexual intercourse.

The fusion event takes place in the **oviduct**.

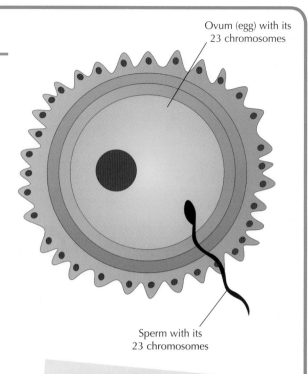

Ovum (egg) with its 23 chromosomes

Sperm with its 23 chromosomes

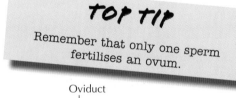

TOP TIP

Remember that only one sperm fertilises an ovum.

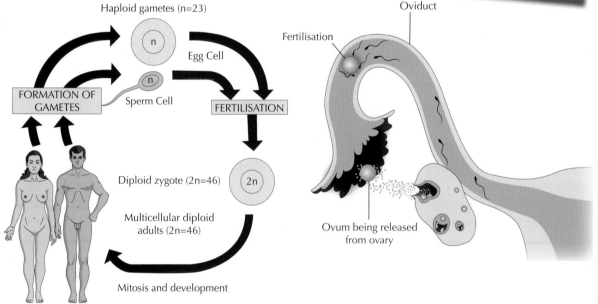

Haploid gametes (n=23)

n

Egg Cell

n

FORMATION OF GAMETES

Sperm Cell

FERTILISATION

Diploid zygote (2n=46)

2n

Multicellular diploid adults (2n=46)

Mitosis and development

Oviduct

Fertilisation

Ovum being released from ovary

In plants, the male gamete inside the pollen grain fuses with the female gamete inside the ovule. To reach the ovule, the pollen grain first has to grow a **pollen tube** down which the male gamete travels. The fertilisation event takes place inside the ovule to form a zygote.

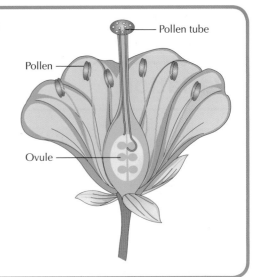

Pollen tube

Pollen

Ovule

TOP TIP

Don't confuse fertilisation (fusion of male and female gametes) with pollination (transfer of pollen) in plants.

Quick Test

1. Give two ways in which the structure of a sperm and the structure of an egg differ.

2. If a cell in the leaf of a flowering plant contains 8 chromosomes, how many chromosomes would be found in an ovule?

3. What is the significance of gametes carrying unique combinations of genetic material from the parent organism which produced them?

Variation and inheritance

Variation

TOP TIP

If a difference can be measured on a balance, by a stopwatch or by a ruler it is nearly always a continuous variation; if not, it is discrete variation.

Living things differ from species to species and within the same species. Such differences are called **variation**. Variation takes two different forms, **discrete** (sometimes called **discontinuous**) variation and **continuous variation**.

Discrete variations include eye colour, right and left handedness and flower colour, while continuous variations include weight, height, rate of heartbeat, length of leaves and number of petals.

Phenotype

The appearance of a plant or animal is a direct result of the genes that are inherited from the parents. The random formation of this combination of genes gives rise to variation, while the actual expression of the genes, often the 'outward appearance' of an individual, is called the **phenotype**. The phenotype may not always be 'outward', for example, in the case of a person's blood grouping.

TOP TIP

Skin colour and weight are also well-known examples of polygenic inheritance.

Some **monogenic** features such as tongue-rolling ability and the presence or absence of ear lobes in humans, plant height in rice and shape of fruit in sweet peppers are controlled by only one gene.

Most features of an individual's phenotype are not monogenically controlled but are under the influence of many genes. This is called **polygenic inheritance**, which is often affected by the environment.

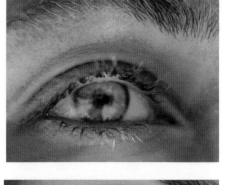

Polygenic inheritance normally shows continuous variation and typically shows a distribution that is termed 'normal'. Height is a well understood example of polygenic inheritance. People are not just short or tall but show variation in heights. Height is influenced by the environment. A person born with the genes to become tall may indeed not fulfil their potential because of a lack of food or disease of some kind.

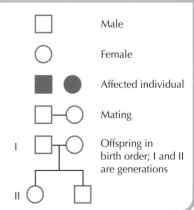

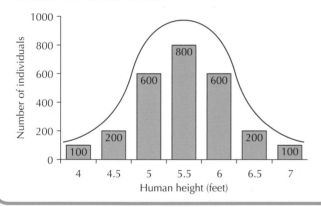

Family trees

Using **family trees** is one way of recording patterns in inheritance. They are often used to help people with a history of genetic diseases, but are used widely in animal and plant genetics. Typically, in animal family trees, the same symbols are commonly used.

□ Male

○ Female

■ ● Affected individual

□—○ Mating

I □—○ Offspring in birth order; I and II are generations

II ○ □

Albinism is a condition in humans that results in a lack of skin pigmentation. Family trees are often used to give advice to people of risks to themselves or their children; born, or unborn. This is called **genetic counselling**.

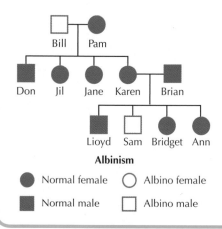

How characteristics are passed on from one generation to another is called **inheritance**. Such characteristics are controlled by genes, which exist in pairs and are found on the chromosomes. Since chromosomes are normally inherited in equal numbers from each parent, one member of each pair of genes comes from the male and one from the female parent. Genes can exist in different forms called **alleles** usually represented by letters. Different alleles of a gene can be **dominant** or **recessive**. A **homozygous** individual has two alleles of a gene (that might be both dominant or both recessive). A **heterozygous** individual has two different forms of a gene, one recessive and one dominant. The combination of the alleles (two dominant, two recessive or one of each) is called the **genotype**.

Inheritance

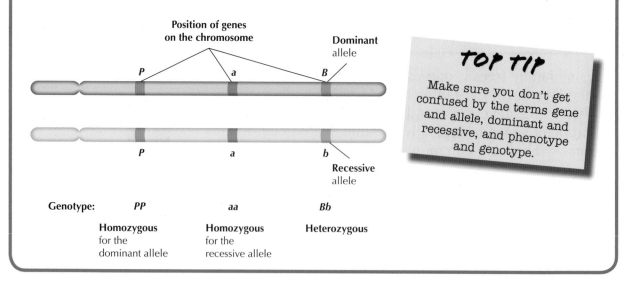

Usually, the upper case letter represents the dominant allele and the lower case letter represents the recessive allele.

One of the first people to suggest a mechanism for inheritance was Gregor Mendel. He worked with garden pea plants that varied in their flower colour, pea shape, height and other characteristics. He suggested that the gametes of each parent could only pass on one member of a pair of alleles. When the gametes fused, the phenotype of the new plants would depend on the various possible combinations of the alleles. The parents formed the **parental generation** and the next generation were called the **first filial (or F₁) generation** and the generation after that, the **second filial (or F₂) generation**.

The small box used to work out the offspring produced is called a **Punnett square**.

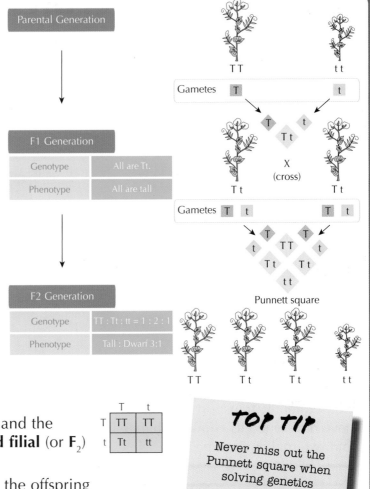

Parental Generation

TT   tt

Gametes   T   t

X (cross)

Tt   Tt

F1 Generation

| Genotype | All are Tt. |
| Phenotype | All are tall |

Gametes T t   T t

Punnett square

F2 Generation

| Genotype | TT : Tt : tt = 1 : 2 : 1 |
| Phenotype | Tall : Dwarf 3:1 |

TT   Tt   Tt   tt

	T	t
T	TT	TT
t	Tt	tt

TOP TIP

Never miss out the Punnett square when solving genetics questions.

Quick Test

1. In pea plants, flower colour is determined by a gene that can exist in two different forms. The dominant (P) gives rise to a purple-coloured flower while the recessive (p) gives rise to a white-coloured flower. Two homozygous, differently coloured flowers were crossed to produce the F₁ generation. Two of these F₁ plants were crossed to produce the F₂ generation, which consisted of 270 purple-flowered plants and 90 white-coloured plants. What was the ratio (expressed as a simple whole number) of purple to white flowers?

2. Copy and complete this table by inserting the different human characteristics under the correct headings.

   height – weight – eye colour – hair length – hair colour

Type of variation	
Continuous	Discrete

3. What is meant by 'polygenic inheritance'?

The need for transport

Need for transport systems

Multicellular organisms have to exchange substances, such as oxygen and carbon dioxide, with their environment. However, because of their size, not all the body cells of a multicellular organism are in contact with their environment. While simpler, unicellular organisms can rely on diffusion, osmosis and active transport, as organisms get larger, their volume increases faster than their surface area, which just isn't able to match the demands of all the cells.

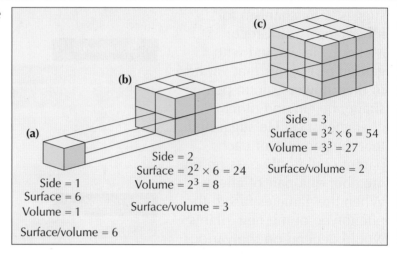

(a)
Side = 1
Surface = 6
Volume = 1
Surface/volume = 6

(b)
Side = 2
Surface = $2^2 \times 6 = 24$
Volume = $2^3 = 8$
Surface/volume = 3

(c)
Side = 3
Surface = $3^2 \times 6 = 54$
Volume = $3^3 = 27$
Surface/volume = 2

Consequently, transport systems in plants and animals have developed to allow exchange between the internal and external environments.

TOP TIP

Be aware that as an organism grows, its surface area to volume ratio is reduced.

Plant transport systems

In almost all multicellular organisms, water is needed for transporting materials.

The movement of water in plants from the roots to the leaves is called the **transpiration stream**, while the actual loss of water by evaporation from a plant is called **transpiration**. Most of the evaporative loss takes place through the leaves but some also takes place from the stems and flowers in plants.

TOP TIP

Remember water is needed for photosynthesis as well as transport in a plant.

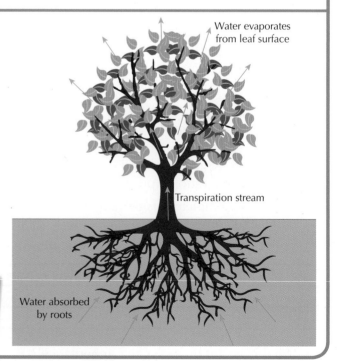

Water evaporates from leaf surface

Transpiration stream

Water absorbed by roots

Water loss from leaves takes place through tiny openings called **stomata** (singular **stoma**) found in the surface layers or **upper** and **lower epidermis** of the leaf. Covering the upper epidermis is a waxy layer called the **cuticle**, which helps cut down water loss. The opening and closing of the stomata is controlled by **guard cells** on either side. Below the upper epidermis is the **palisade layer** consisting of tall, cylindrically-shaped cells, where most photosynthesis takes place.

TOP TIP

Palisade cells are packed with chloroplasts as an adaptation for their function in photosynthesis and their shape allows many to be packed close together.

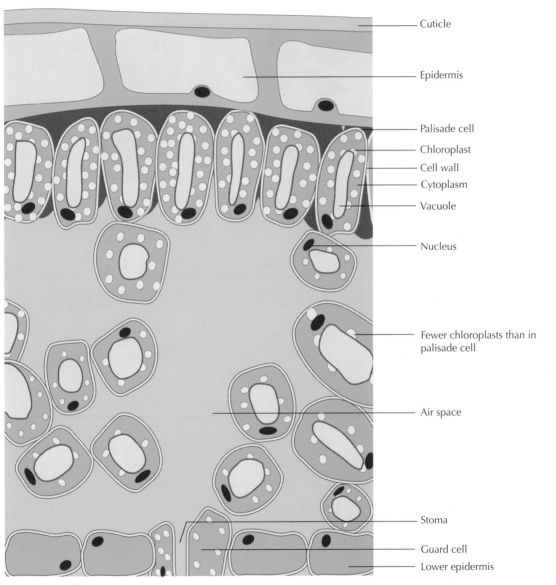

Cuticle

Epidermis

Palisade cell

Chloroplast

Cell wall

Cytoplasm

Vacuole

Nucleus

Fewer chloroplasts than in palisade cell

Air space

Stoma

Guard cell

Lower epidermis

The **spongy mesophyll layer** consists of irregularly shaped cells that do not fit together, allowing many air spaces between them. The air can circulate freely among these cells and so reach the other cells inside the leaf.

Water enters by osmosis through the roots via special **root hair cells**, which have a very large surface area for absorption.

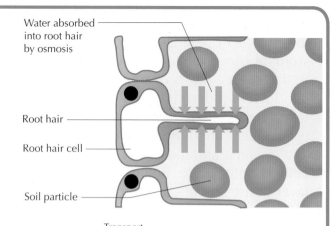

Water absorbed into root hair by osmosis

Root hair

Root hair cell

Soil particle

Within the plant a transport system moves water up from the roots to the leaves in the form of narrow tubes called **xylem**, arranged near the outside of the stem. Close to the xylem is the **phloem** which transports food from the leaves to all parts of the plant.

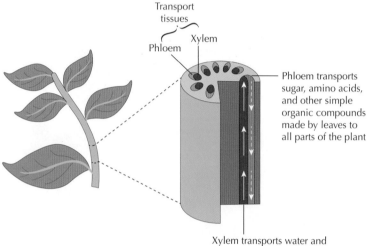

Transport tissues

Phloem

Xylem

Phloem transports sugar, amino acids, and other simple organic compounds made by leaves to all parts of the plant

Xylem transports water and dissolved substances from the roots to the leaves

Lignin

To withstand changes in pressure as water travels through the xylem, these cells are strengthened with a material called **lignin**.

TOP TIP

Mature tall trees rely on lignin to support them.

As water evaporates from the surfaces of a plant, more water is drawn up to replace it. This creates a pull that is sufficient to support a very tall column of water, many metres in length.

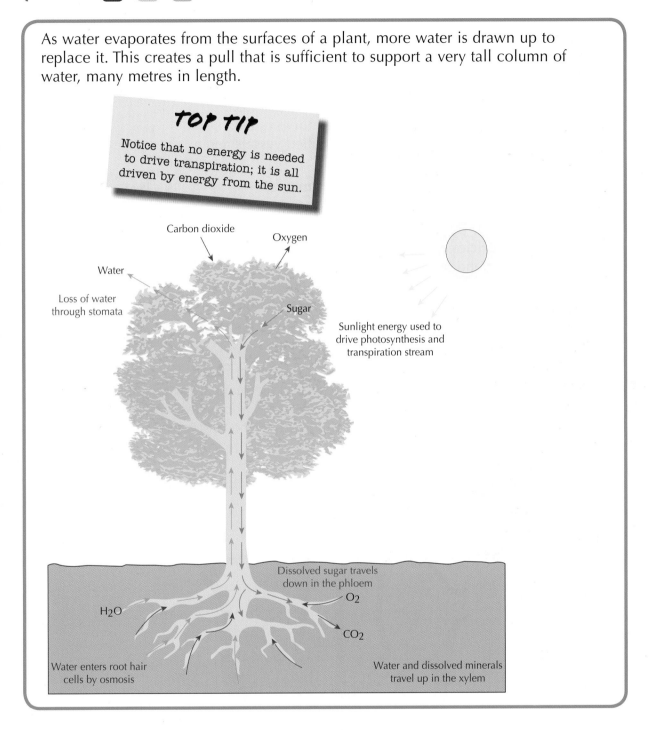

TOP TIP

Notice that no energy is needed to drive transpiration; it is all driven by energy from the sun.

Carbon dioxide

Oxygen

Water

Loss of water through stomata

Sugar

Sunlight energy used to drive photosynthesis and transpiration stream

Dissolved sugar travels down in the phloem

O_2

H_2O

CO_2

Water enters root hair cells by osmosis

Water and dissolved minerals travel up in the xylem

Quick Test

1. Give three advantages of transpiration to a plant.
2. Explain why water will travel up the xylem more quickly on a dry day than on a humid day.
3. What is the function of lignin in xylem?

Animal transport and exchange systems

In mammals, blood transports vital nutrients and oxygen to every cell in the body and removes carbon dioxide from every cell. This is carried out by the **circulatory system**, which consists of blood moving in tubes called **vessels** and a pump called the **heart**.

The heart consists of four spaces called **chambers**.

The two upper chambers, or **atria** (singular **atrium**) receive blood from the body or the lungs while the two lower chambers, or **ventricles**, discharge blood to the lungs or to the body. Both the left and right sides of the heart have an atrium and a ventricle. **Valves** in the heart ensure that there is no backflow of blood and that blood flows in one direction only.

Blood flows into the heart through **veins** and out of the heart through **arteries**.

> ### TOP TIP
> The heart is really two pumps that beat as one unit. The left side deals with blood rich in oxygen while the right side deals with blood low in oxygen.

> ### TOP TIP
> Remember: <u>A</u>rteries carry blood <u>A</u>way from the heart and <u>V</u>eins have <u>V</u>alves.

Like the heart, veins have valves to prevent backflow of blood. The main vein returning blood to the heart is the **vena cava** and the main artery taking blood from the heart is the **aorta**. The atria, which receive blood from veins, are thin-walled because they do not pump blood very far. However, the ventricles are both thick-walled because they have to pump blood under pressure to the lungs or to the rest

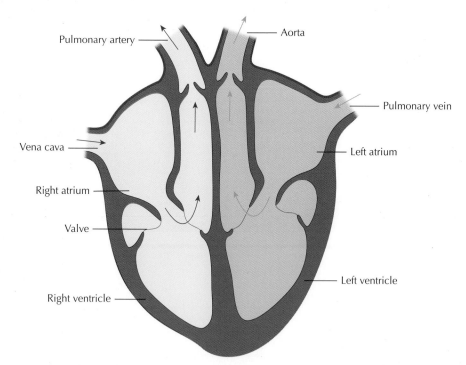

of the body. The **pulmonary artery** carries blood low in oxygen from the right ventricle to the lungs while the **pulmonary vein** carries blood rich in oxygen from the lungs to the left atrium.

All over the body are found **capillaries**, which connect arteries and veins. As blood flows through capillaries, exchange of gases, nutrients and wastes takes place through their thin walls, which are only one-cell thick.

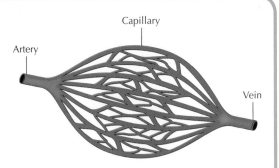

The circuit of blood involves a return of deoxygenated blood to the right side of the heart from the body and then from the right side to the lungs. From the lungs, the oxygenated blood returns to the left side of the heart and then from the left side out to the body again.

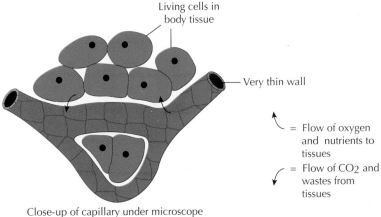

Close-up of capillary under microscope

↑ = Flow of oxygen and nutrients to tissues

↓ = Flow of CO_2 and wastes from tissues

TOP TIP

Capillaries have an enormous surface area for exchange of materials and are very close to every single cell in the body.

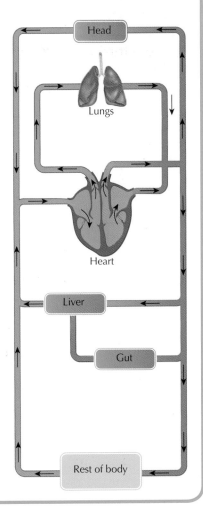

Arteries and veins differ in their structure and function.

Artery	Vein
Close-up of artery Thick muscular wall	Close-up of vein Valve Thin muscular wall
Transports blood away from heart	Transports blood to the heart
Carries blood rich in oxygen	Carries blood low in oxygen
Has a relatively small diameter	Has a relatively large diameter
Walls are very muscular	Walls have little muscle
Walls are very elastic	Walls are not very elastic
No valves are present	Valves are present
Blood is under high pressure	Blood is under low pressure
Ends in capillaries	Formed from capillaries
Pulse can be easily felt	Pulse not easily felt
Usually situated deep in body tissue	Usually situated nearer the skin

TOP TIP

The pulmonary artery and pulmonary vein are both exceptions to the general rule about arteries carrying blood rich in oxygen and veins carrying blood low in oxygen.

Blood

Red blood cells are the most numerous of the cells found in the blood, making up about a quarter of the cells of the human body! A single drop of blood contains millions of red blood cells, which are constantly travelling through the body to supply cells with oxygen. They are unusual in having no nucleus or other structures such as mitochondria or ribosomes inside, leaving all the available space to contain as much of the protein **haemoglobin** as possible.

Haemoglobin is the carrier molecule that combines with oxygen in the lungs and then releases it at respiring cells. It also gives blood its red colour. Red blood cells are doughnut shaped (without the hole), which gives them a huge surface area to pick up and release oxygen across their membranes. The cells are also very flexible so they can squeeze through capillaries in single-file.

After about 120 days, a red blood cell wears out, eventually dies and is replaced by new ones produced within material inside bones called **marrow**. Red blood cells are produced at a staggering rate of about 2 million per second in a healthy adult!

TOP TIP

The structure of a red blood cell is ideally suited to its function.

Lungs

The actual exchange of the gases oxygen and carbon dioxide takes place in the lungs, which are the main organs of the breathing system.

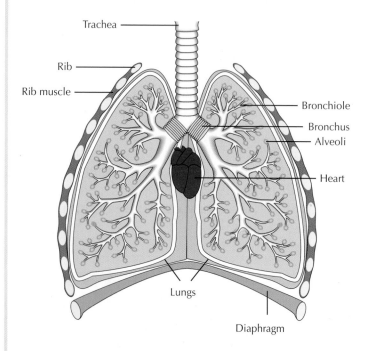

The lungs have a huge surface area, which allows oxygen and carbon dioxide to diffuse quickly to and from the blood. However, as diffusion on its own is not rapid enough we have special muscles between the ribs, which cause air to be pulled in and pushed out much more quickly. The **trachea** is lined with tiny 'hairs' called **cilia**, which, in conjunction with a sticky material called **mucus**, trap dust and germs. These are then passed up to the nose and mouth to be expelled by sneezing, or coughing or swallowed into the stomach to be destroyed there. To enable us to breathe freely, the trachea must be open at all times, even when we bend our neck. It is kept open by incomplete rings of an elastic material called **cartilage**.

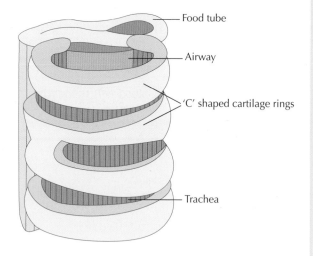

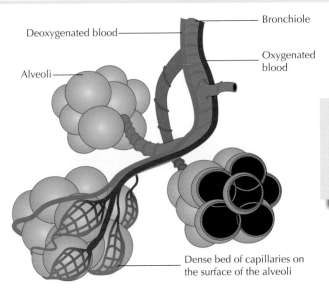

Deoxygenated blood

Alveoli

Bronchiole

Oxygenated blood

Dense bed of capillaries on the surface of the alveoli

The ends of the **bronchioles** consist of tiny little air sacs called **alveoli** where gas exchange takes place.

TOP TIP

Alveoli are adapted for their function by being thin-walled, having a dense blood supply, a moist lining and a huge surface area.

Blood flows through the lungs in capillaries, which are in very close contact with the alveoli. Oxygen diffuses from the alveoli into the blood in the capillaries and carbon dioxide diffuses from the blood in the capillaries into the alveoli. Since there are millions of alveoli in each lung, the overall surface area for gas exchange is enormous.

Air is moved in and out of the breathing system during inhalation and exhalation using the rib muscles and the **diaphragm**.

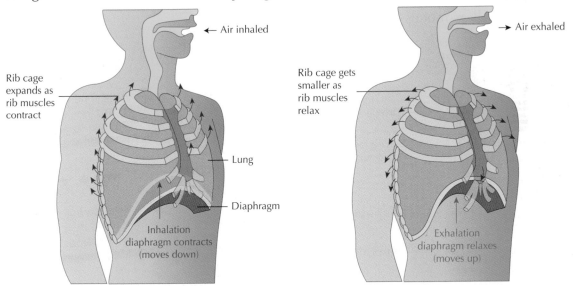

← Air inhaled

Rib cage expands as rib muscles contract

Lung

Diaphragm

Inhalation diaphragm contracts (moves down)

→ Air exhaled

Rib cage gets smaller as rib muscles relax

Exhalation diaphragm relaxes (moves up)

When breathing in (inhalation), the rib muscles and diaphragm contract, increasing the volume in the chest cavity. This lowers the pressure inside the lungs causing them to expand and draw air in.

When breathing out (exhalation), the rib muscles and diaphragm relax, decreasing the volume in the chest cavity. This increases pressure inside the lungs causing them to deflate and push air out.

The digestive system

After we have eaten, food is broken up into small pieces until, eventually, the large molecules of fat, protein and carbohydrate are fully broken down into small molecular products to be transported in the blood and used by every cell in the body. Thus food is both mechanically and chemically broken down from large pieces into small pieces and large molecules into small molecules.

Mechanical and chemical digestion starts in the mouth where our teeth break up the food into small pieces. Saliva is added, which helps to make the food slide down the **oesophagus** into the stomach.

Saliva contains an enzyme called **amylase** which starts the breakdown of starch, converting it into the sugar **maltose** as well as mucus

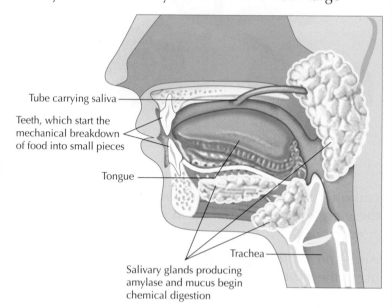

Tube carrying saliva

Teeth, which start the mechanical breakdown of food into small pieces

Tongue

Trachea

Salivary glands producing amylase and mucus begin chemical digestion

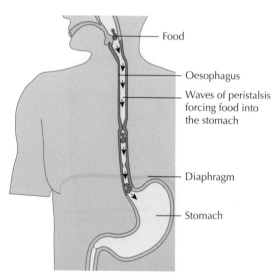

Food

Oesophagus

Waves of peristalsis forcing food into the stomach

Diaphragm

Stomach

to make the food easier to swallow. As food travels along the digestive system, different parts contribute towards converting the food into a form that can be used by body cells.

After chewing food and mixing it with saliva, food is passed down the oesophagus into the stomach by peristaltic waves.

> **TOP TIP**
> Chewing food exposes a large surface area for enzymes to act on.

> **TOP TIP**
> Swallowing is an example of a reflex action.

In the stomach, digestive enzymes and hydrochloric acid are added to food to continue the breakdown process. The partially digested food now enters the **small intestine** to complete digestion and allow **absorption** to take place.

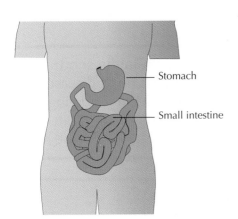

Stomach

Small intestine

Inner lining covered with villi

The small intestine is highly adapted for the process of absorption. Its inner lining is covered with many tiny finger-like structures called **villi**, which hugely increase the surface area. Villi have a number of structural adaptions making them well suited to their function:

- covering is only one-cell thick so that digested food has a short distance to travel to enter the blood
- dense blood supply in the form of many capillaries for absorption of sugars, amino acids, water, minerals and many vitamins.

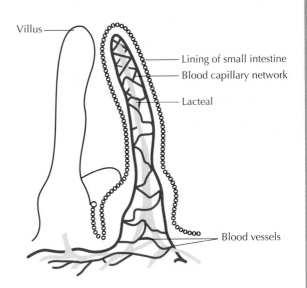

Villus

Lining of small intestine

Blood capillary network

Lacteal

Blood vessels

In the centre of each villus is found a **lacteal** which absorbs the end-products of the digestion of fats called **fatty acids** and **glycerol**. Lacteals connect with a 'secondary transport system' called the **lymphatic system** by means of a fluid called **lymph**.

Blood carries all the products of digestion, except those of fat, towards the liver. Digested fats are carried in lymphatic vessels in lymph towards the heart where they enter the blood stream.

Quick Test

1. Name two vital substances, transported in the blood, which are needed by the heart muscle.
2. How is the trachea adapted to prevent dust and germs from entering?
3. What is meant by the 'mechanical breakdown' of food?

The effect of lifestyle choices on animal transport and exchange systems

The choices humans make about their lifestyle affect health both in the short and long-term. These choices impact on the risks associated with heart disease, stroke, diabetes, liver problems, lung disease and some cancers. The following five lifestyle choices are known to affect the physical and mental health of an individual as well as impacting on the quality of life and immunity to disease.

Smoking

Smokers become addicted to the chemical, **nicotine**, found in tobacco. This chemical, on inhalation of cigarette smoke, reaches the brain in less than 10 seconds where it stimulates the nervous system and generally relaxes muscles. Long-term smoking causes arteries to narrow, increasing blood pressure; nicotine also increases the tendency of blood to clot. Less oxygen can travel to the brain as the haemoglobin in the red blood cells combines with carbon monoxide found in the smoke. Tar in cigarette smoke has a paralysing effect on the cilia lining the breathing system. It also irritates the lungs and stimulates them to produce more mucus, which builds up as the cilia are unable to perform their function properly. This leads to the characteristic 'smoker's cough'. Lung diseases, such as **bronchitis** and **emphysema**, occur more frequently in smokers.

TOP TIP

Emphysema seriously reduces the surface area available for gas exchange in the lungs.

There are more than 4000 different chemicals in cigarette smoke, some of which are known to cause cancer in the lungs. More than 90% of all lung cancers are thought to be linked to smoking. This risk is increased if people:

- live in areas of air pollution
- passively inhale smoke from others
- start smoking when very young
- smoke many cigarettes each day
- smoke cigarettes which have no filter attached
- inhale the smoke.

Pregnant women who smoke also put their unborn babies at risk because many of the harmful chemicals found in cigarette smoke can move across the placenta.

TOP TIP

An unborn child of a mother who smokes receives less oxygen than normal and this can result in a smaller birth weight.

Regular exercise

Regular exercise is known to have many beneficial effects such as:

- increasing life expectancy
- decreasing the risk of early death due to heart disease
- helping to reduce the risk of developing diabetes
- reducing blood pressure
- reducing risks to certain cancers, such as cancer of the large intestine
- promoting a feeling of well-being
- controlling weight
- maintain good muscle tone and healthy bones and joints.

Exercise which causes a mild shortness of breath and perhaps a little sweating is fine. For example, jogging, brisk walks, gardening, cycling, playing sports, etc.

Healthy diet

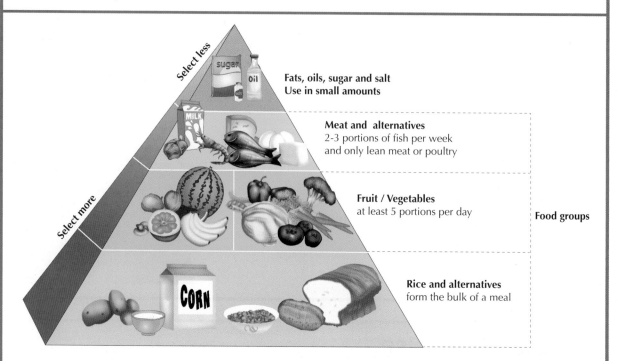

A healthy diet can be thought of as an 'eating pyramid': the foods near the top should be eaten in small quantities only.

Starch-based foods (such as rice, pasta, wholegrain bread, cereal, potatoes) should form the bulk of most meals.

The recommended intake of a variety of fruit and vegetables is at least five portions per day. If possible, two to three portions of fish per week should include at least one 'oily' fish such as herring, mackerel, sardines, fresh tuna, kippers, pilchards or salmon. Red Meat should be lean or poultry eaten as an alternative. When possible, fried food should be avoided or fried only in a vegetable-based oil such as olive, sunflower or rapeseed. Fatty foods should only be eaten occasionally and in small quantities. These include fatty meats, hard cheeses, full-cream milk, cream, butter and fried food. Adding extra salt to food should also be avoided.

A balanced diet includes vitamins and minerals essential for health. Iron for example, is necessary to make haemoglobin; if deficient, **anaemia** will result.

TOP TIP

Fats and added salt can be 'hidden' in foods.

Losing weight

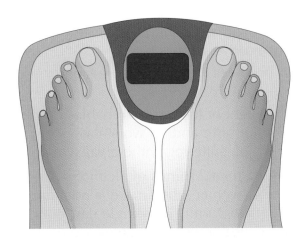

It is now quite easy to find out what the correct body mass is in relation to size and other variables. Being overweight puts additional stress on the heart and circulatory system as well as increasing blood pressure. If you are overweight and attaining the ideal weight is too difficult, great health benefits are obtained by losing 5–10% of your weight. Over half the population in Scotland are overweight or obese which means most people eat more than they need.

TOP TIP

Weight increases when the energy intake is more than the energy used by the body.

Over time, extra intake of food leads to weight gain; this in turn increases the risk factors mentioned. Drinks also are energy-rich! Fat-rich diets can cause deposits called **atheroma** in blood vessels restricting blood flow and provoking blood clots.

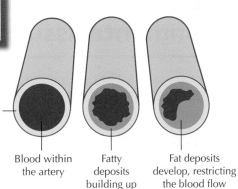

Artery wall

Blood within the artery

Fatty deposits building up

Fat deposits develop, restricting the blood flow through the artery.

Taking alcohol in moderation

Although technically a drug, alcohol is very commonly available and forms part of our social life. The measurement of alcohol content in drinks can vary but usually, in the context of moderating intake, it is expressed as 'units'. Approximately, one unit is equivalent to half a pint of lager or beer, or two-thirds of a small glass of wine, or one small pub measure of spirits. Alcohol is absorbed very quickly and does not need to be digested. It enters the bloodstream within about 2 minutes of being swallowed. It takes our bodies

roughly 60 minutes to remove one unit. Being careful about alcohol intake is important for several reasons:

- long term use of alcohol can have a negative effect on health. For example, the liver, stomach and kidneys in particular can be badly damaged.

- alcohol affects co-ordination, judgement and self-control. This can cause anti-social behaviour and the inability to drive safely.

- over a long period, memory function becomes impaired; depression may also result

- pregnant women can affect the development of their unborn babies by drinking alcohol. Babies are usually underweight at birth and, in worst-case scenarios, can be born with a dependence on alcohol, suffering withdrawal symptoms.

In the UK men are advised not to drink more than 21 units of alcohol per week and no more than 4 units in a single day. For women, the advice is no more than 14 units of alcohol per week and no more than 3 units in a single day. Both men and women should have two alcohol-free days per week. Pregnant women should not drink at all.

Environmental issues

The environment we choose to live also impacts on our health. **Pollution** of environment is any addition to the water, or air which might cause short or long-damage to the natural ecological balance the earth and/or the quality of life.

This pollution could be sewage unwanted chemicals or energy in the form heat or nuclear or sound. Nowadays, it recognised that pollution is no longer a localised issue and many of the choices made affect people in different parts of the world.

TOP TIP

Pollution can take many forms such as litter, noise, or unsightly buildings, which impact on people's lives.

Radiation

The use of nuclear devices and power stations causes the formation of radiation to rise above its normal level. Some industrial and laboratory processes can produce radiation as a by-product, such as scientific devices that emit Gamma rays. Even at a more local level, the use of X-rays in medicine, mobile telephones, radio transmitters and microwave ovens produce radiation. We now know the harmful effects that exposure to radiation can have on living material. These include radiation sickness, genetic damage and cancers. In addition, unborn babies can suffer brain damage if exposed to excess radiation; this can affect their intelligence and possibly cause mental retardation.

TOP TIP

Pregnant women are not X-rayed unless it is necessary because of the potential damage the radiation might cause to the developing baby

Heavy metals

Chemical elements with an atomic number greater than 20 include the **heavy metals** such as lead, mercury, arsenic, and cadmium. These are known to be highly toxic to human tissue. They can enter the human food chain via food, water, air or through the skin. Once inside the body, they can compete for essential heavy metals such as cobalt, iron, copper, zinc, manganese and molybdenum which are needed in humans in trace amounts. This displacement of required heavy metals can cause illness through poisoning, sometimes over a long period of time. Since heavy metals cannot easily be removed from human tissues, they tend to accumulate, increasing in concentration.
This is called **bioaccumulation**. In the short-term, heavy metals in relatively low quantities can cause headaches, depression, raised blood pressure and cholesterol levels, lack of energy, increases in weight, inability to concentrate and forgetfulness. Longer-term exposure can lead to irreversible changes in organ function, such as cancer.

TOXIC HAZARD

Quick Test

1. Why is an unborn baby at risk if the mother smokes during pregnancy?
2. What is atheroma and how is it harmful to the circulation of the blood?
3. Why is it not safe to drive if 'over the legal limit'?

End of Unit Questions

Section A

1. Which of the following descriptions is correct?

	Tissue	Organ	System
A	Xylem	Phloem	Photosynthetic
B	Stem	Leaf	Transport
C	Sperm	Testis	Reproductive
D	Nerve	Brain	Nervous

2. Which of the following pairs of responses are both examples of reflex actions?

   A Sneezing and standing up

   B Coughing and scratching itchy skin

   C Breathing and speaking

   D Vomiting and blinking

3. The diagram below shows a human brain.

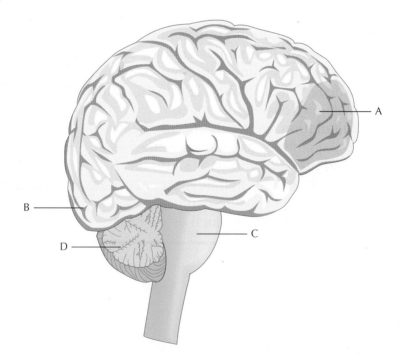

   Which part regulates the heartbeat?

4. Which one of the following properties of glycogen is not correct? Glycogen:

   A can be used directly by the brain as a quick source of energy

   B being insoluble, does not set up any osmotic effects

   C is an ideal form of energy storage

   D is a large molecule formed from many smaller units

5. Which one of the following pieces of apparatus could be used to compare the relative amount of carbon dioxide in inhaled air with that in exhaled air by breathing in and out at the mouthpiece shown as M?

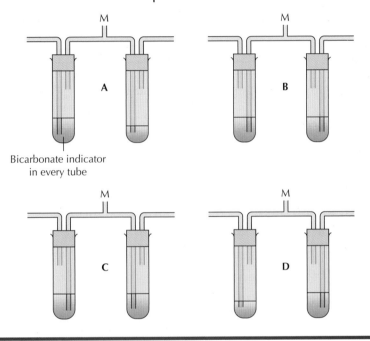

Bicarbonate indicator in every tube

Section B

1. Copy the information below and connect the terms on the left to the correct statements on the right by means of arrow-headed lines.

diploid	number of chromosomes in sperms
haploid	fertilised egg
gonad	generalised name for a sex cell
gamete	number of chromosomes in plant body
zygote	structure where sex cells are manufactured

[2]

2. (a) What is meant by 'monogenic inheritance'? [1]

   (b) Give two examples of monogenic inheritance. [1]

3. In a particular type of dog, the coat may be a plain pattern or a spotted pattern. Plain pattern (S) is dominant while spotted pattern (s) is recessive.

   (a) A spotted dog is crossed with a heterozygous plain-patterned dog.
       (i) What are the possible phenotypes of the offspring? [1]
       (ii) What are the possible genotypes of the offspring? [1]

   (b) A heterozygous plain patterned dog is mated with another heterozygous solid patterned dog.

       What is the genotypic ratio of the offspring? [1]

4. Copy and complete the following paragraph by inserting the correct words into the spaces provided.

   Water is moved from the roots to the leaves in the _____ and dissolved sugar is moved from the leaves to the roots in the _____ [1]

5. Copy and complete the following table. [2]

	Artery	Vein	Capillary
Relative diameter	Small		
Wall		Thin Muscular	
Valves			Absent

6. A student investigated how feedback might improve a person's ability to draw a line of a certain length. Three male volunteers were separately first shown a line that was exactly 8 cm long, drawn on paper. Next, each volunteer in turn was seated as shown in the diagram to the right and asked to draw a line of 8 cm on 5 consecutive sheets of paper that were behind a wooden screen. The volunteer was asked not to touch the table as he drew the lines. Before the 6th attempt, the volunteer was told the average of his previous 5 attempts and then given a further 5 attempts. The data obtained are shown in the table.

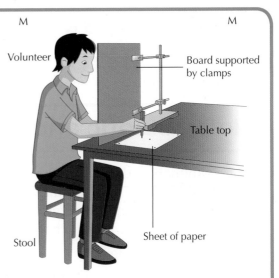

Attempt	Length of lines drawn (cm)		
	Volunteer 1	Volunteer 2	Volunteer 3
1	8·1	6·0	4·5
2	7·9	6·7	5·5
3	7·7	8·3	7·5
4	8·2	8·2	8·5
5	7·6	8·3	5·0
Average			
6	7·9	6·2	5·5
7	7·9	6·6	5·8
8	8·1	8·3	9·0
9	8·1	8·1	7·8
10	8·0	7·8	7·9
Average			

(a) Copy and complete the table by calculating the average results for each volunteer. Then create a bar chart showing the average results of the first and second attempts of the three volunteers. [4]

(b) What is the dependent variable in this investigation? [1]

(c) The student concluded that feedback improved a person's ability to draw a line of a certain length.

Give two reasons why this was not a valid conclusion. [2]

(d) How could the reliability of the results be improved? [1]

(e) State two ways in which the student could improve the design of this investigation. [1]

Biodiversity and the distribution of life

Biotic, abiotic and human influences

Plants, animals and micro-organisms are found everywhere on planet Earth. A living thing lives in a **habitat**. The range of living things that are found in an environment is called **biodiversity** and is often delicately balanced. It can be affected by different factors that may be **biotic** or **abiotic**.

Biotic factors include:

- competition for food, space, mates
- numbers of predators
- disease
- grazing.

Abiotic factors include:

- temperature
- humidity
- pH
- light intensity
- rainfall
- wind.

Humans can influence their local, national and global environments by such as activities as:

- pollution of the air or water
- destruction of natural habitats
- exploitation of animals and plants.

TOP TIP

Think of the different ways in which humans can destroy natural habitats.

Grazing, predation, effect of pH and temperature

Herbivores, such as zebra, antelope etc. feed by grazing on plant life. The effect this grazing has on biodiversity depends on the level of the grazing. At low grazing intensity, dominant plants may prevail making it difficult or impossible for more delicate forms to survive, thus reducing biodiversity. At high grazing intensity, perhaps due

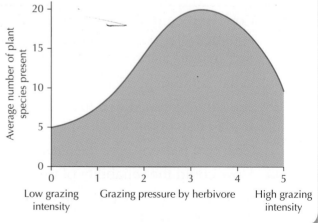

Average number of plant species present (y-axis: 0, 5, 10, 15, 20)

Grazing pressure by herbivore (x-axis: 0, 1, 2, 3, 4, 5)

Low grazing intensity — High grazing intensity

to increased population numbers, less and less of the plant life can survive as the herbivores compete for shared resources. This also decreases biodiversity. With a balanced interaction between grazers and their food sources, native plants and grasses will prosper because they don't have to compete with the more aggressive surrounding non-native species. Grazers have a positive effect on biodiversity too. They often push seeds into soft soil with their feet and these seeds germinate later. They also fertilise the soil with their waste products.

Recent work has shown that predation is a critical factor in maintaining high levels of biodiversity. For example, the decline in certain large cats in some national parks has allowed deer and similar mammals to reproduce in large numbers, with the loss of many plant species that are, in turn, eaten by these animals. The loss of plant species brings about soil erosion, while pollinators, such as bees and butterflies, may no longer have suitable sources of pollen. Similarly, populations of wild foxes and cats may spiral uncontrolled if their natural predators reduce in numbers; this in turn may drastically reduce the numbers and types of their food.

Fish are generally very sensitive to changes in the pH and temperature of the water. Most aquatic environments have a pH that is nearly neutral, around 7. If this is lowered or increased by pollution it can interfere with the reproductive life cycles of fish as well as promoting the invasive growth of plants which cannot grow at pH 7, reducing the number of fish species. Some processes, such as generating power, use vast quantities of water as a coolant. This warmer water, when discharged back into rivers and streams, can elevate the temperature of rivers and streams where fish thrive. A similar effect is caused by global warming. In water that is warmer than normal, fish mature quicker but produce fewer offspring. The amount of dissolved oxygen in warm water is less and this, coupled with an increased rate of respiration, causes many fish eventually to die out.

Biomes

Life is found almost everywhere on planet Earth but specific regions exist that share similar climates, animal and plant life (**fauna** and **flora**). These are known as **biomes**.

Like any region, a biome is affected by both temperature and rainfall because these abiotic factors in turn influence the fauna and flora that can survive there.

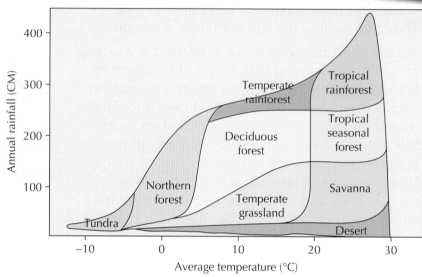

Ecosystems

In an environment, such as a woodland or pond, individual living things form **populations**: a group consisting of only one species. Together, populations form different **communities** and with their environment communities form an **ecosystem**. Ecosystems form different biomes, which, collectively, form the **biosphere** itself: the part of the Earth's surface and atmosphere within which life can exist.

Many different types of ecosystems are possible such as:

- desert
- forest
- pond
- river
- estuary
- heather moorland
- arctic tundra
- coral reefs

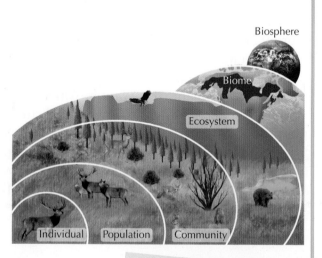

Niches

In their environment, living things perform particular roles called **niches**. The actual niche an organism lives in is dependent on the food eaten and the impact of variables such as:

- light intensity
- temperature
- competition
- parasitism
- predation

Branches & leaves : bees, wasps, moths, squirrels, bluetits and hawks

Trunk : insects & larvae

Root & litter zone : bacteria, earthworms, woodlice and fungi

Quick Test

1. Put the following factors under the correct column heading in the table:
temperature – light intensity – predation – humidity – wind – salinity – disease – soil moisture – food availability – space

Abiotic factor	Biotic factor

2. Which term best describes where a plant or animal lives?

3. What does the term 'community' mean?

Energy in ecosystems

Energy loss

To survive, all living things need energy. While animals obtain their energy from respiration, plants rely on the sun. Only a very tiny fraction of the total energy of the sun actually is absorbed by plants and used in photosynthesis.

As plants are eaten by animals and they, in turn, are eaten by other animals, about 90% of the energy gets lost as heat, movement or is trapped in energy-rich wastes passed between each transfer. When an animal or plant dies, the remains are broken down by bacteria, fungi and invertebrates called **decomposers** and a lot of energy is lost as heat to the atmosphere. Only about 10% of the energy taken in by a plant or animal is actually available to the next feeding level.

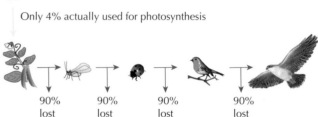

Only 4% actually used for photosynthesis

90% lost   90% lost   90% lost   90% lost

TOP TIP
Most of the energy that hits a leaf is lost as heat or transmitted through the leaf or reflected from it.

TOP TIP
Because so much energy is lost between feeding levels, an ecosystem cannot support large numbers of carnivores.

Pyramids of biomass, energy and numbers

Pyramid diagrams can be used to represent changes in the variables associated with ecosystems. Three different variables can be represented in this way:

1. numbers
2. **biomass** (the total mass of living things in the environment)
3. energy

TOP TIP
The biomass is expressed as dry mass to avoid errors due to the presence or absence of water.

As energy is lost at each feeding level, the number of organisms normally decreases proportionally. This change can be represented by a **pyramid of numbers**.

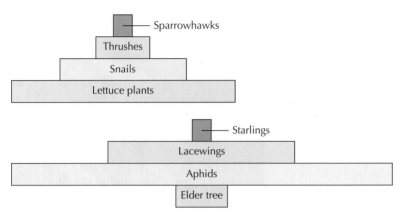

The total biomass from one feeding level to the next one higher up decreases in an ecosystem and this change can be represented by a **pyramid of biomass**.

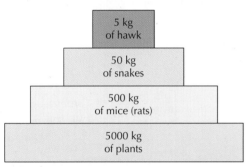 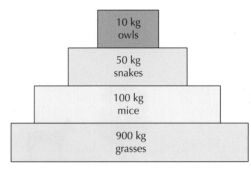

A more valid way of representing the changes that take place from one feeding level to the next is the **pyramid of energy**.

Such pyramids are more difficult to construct; they require a lot of data collected over long periods but give a better picture of how an ecosystem is working.

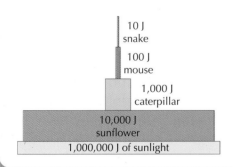 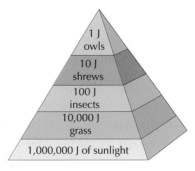

Nitrogen cycle

Almost 80% of our atmosphere is made up of the gas nitrogen, but this is a very unreactive substance and very few organisms can make any use of it directly. However, it is a vital component of many important chemicals necessary for life such as amino acids, proteins, nucleic acids, chlorophyll and adenosine triphosphate. Animals obtain nitrogen from their diet but plants can obtain it in chemical form as nitrates dissolved in soil water or, in some cases, by trapping, or 'fixing' atmospheric nitrogen. To fix the atmospheric nitrogen, some plants use special bacteria found in their roots in small swellings called **root nodules**.

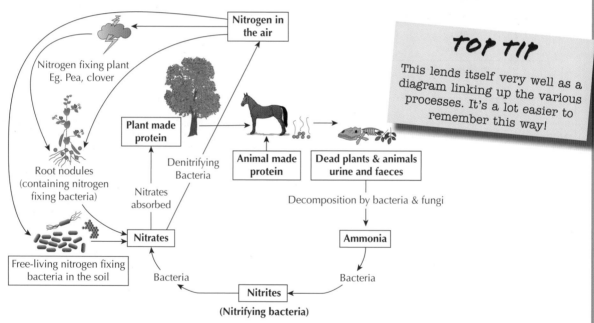

TOP TIP

This lends itself very well as a diagram linking up the various processes. It's a lot easier to remember this way!

The bacteria in the root nodules fix the atmospheric nitrogen and convert this into nitrates in the soil, which the plant can use to make nitrogen-containing chemicals such as nitrates. These bacteria are known as **nitrogen fixing**. Some free-living bacteria found in the soil can also fix atmospheric nitrogen. Other bacteria, found in the soil, called **denitrifying bacteria,** can break down the nitrates to release nitrogen back into the air. Also, as animals and plants die and as they produce wastes, these remains are broken down by decomposers to form ammonia, which is converted to nitrates by **nitrifying bacteria**. These nitrates also become available to plants in the soil. These processes are all linked together to form a nutrient cycle called the **nitrogen cycle**.

If a soil is low in nitrates, growers can add nitrate in the form of fertilisers, either natural, such as animal manure, or artificial in the form of chemicals. This will increase the yield obtained by encouraging plant growth. However, fertilisers should not be applied in excess so that they can be washed out of the soil and into waterways.

Competition

Resources such as space, food, water, light, mates, and shelter are not without limit on Earth; animals and plants have to compete for these, especially if any are in short supply. If the competition is between members of the same species this is called **intraspecific competition** and between members of different species, **interspecific competition**. Competition helps prevent populations of animals and plants becoming too large to be supported by their environment.

Grasshoppers often feed in large swarms that are made up of the same species and all the individuals compete for the same food source.

Animals, such as robins, may compete for the same space known as their **territory** and make this known by their behaviour patterns. For example, a robin's red-coloured breast establishes territorial rights by making them more visible and attractive to potential mates.

In many parts of Scotland, the grey squirrel has reduced the numbers of the native red squirrel. These two different species compete for the same resources but the grey squirrel is more successful.

As cheetahs and lions, which are different animal species, both feed on similar prey, such as gazelles, the presence of one has a negative impact on the other because they both compete for the same food resource.

In any large, well-established forest, many different species of plants will compete for shared resources such as:

- light
- carbon dioxide
- water
- nutrients.

Plants in such a well-established forest have different heights as they receive varying amounts of these shared resources. The different species will compete vigorously; those that are better suited to obtain them will grow best and outperform the weaker plants. The latter may grow poorly or in the long-term be completely wiped out.

Sometimes a non-native plant species can invade and start to dominate a forest, such as in Hawaii when ground-dwelling ferns became established as the dominant plant form.

Quick Test

1.	Give one important role played by decomposers in ecosystems.
2.	What function do denitrifying bacteria perform in the nitrogen cycle?
3.	Explain the difference between 'intraspecific' and 'interspecific' competition.

Sampling techniques and the measurement of biotic and abiotic factors

Sampling techniques

If a groundsman wanted to know how many dandelions were growing in a football pitch, it would be impractical to try to count every single dandelion. Instead, he might select a number of small areas, a process called **sampling**. All the samples would be of the same size and he would count the number of dandelions in each. From this he could calculate an average number of dandelions in one of these small areas and then multiply this up to the actual area of the football pitch.

There are a number of techniques which can be used on their own or together when sampling.

A **quadrat** is a commonly used simple piece of apparatus, usually made of metal, with a known area, often 0.25 m^2. This is laid randomly on the ground and the plants or animals of interest are counted. From this data, an average number of the organisms is obtained. Knowing the actual area being investigated, it is then possible to estimate the number of these organisms present.

Quadrats can be used on land but also along shores and under water.

TOP TIP

Quadrats can also be made of wood or string.

Surface living animals can be sampled using a **pitfall trap**. This is usually a jar or tin can sunk into the soil overnight. The animals fall into the container and can be studied the following day.

A **Tullgren** funnel can be used to extract small invertebrate animals from a soil sample put into a funnel, in the base of which is a mesh that will hold the particles of soil back but allow the invertebrates to pass through. The light and heat from a lamp above the mesh encourages the animals to move in the opposite direction into a collecting container below.

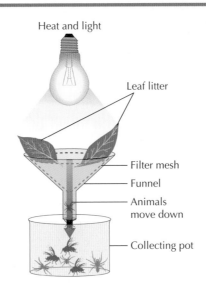

Heat and light

Leaf litter

Filter mesh

Funnel

Animals move down

Collecting pot

A **pooter** can pick up small invertebrates by a sucking action at one end of a tube that draws small animals into the chamber for examination later.

Tree beating involves striking a tree branch with a stout stick causing any small animals to fall out into a collecting tray held underneath.

Using a sweeping action, nets can be used in the air and in water to trap animals that are too large to escape the mesh.

The **transect** method is commonly used in ecology to examine a part of an ecosystem at set intervals along a line.

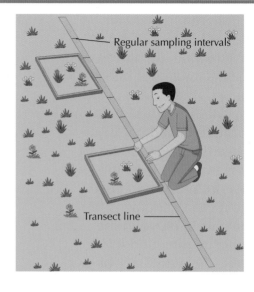

In studying an ecosystem, it is necessary to have data related to the numbers of organisms present but it is rarely possible to count all of these. It might be easy to do this with large animals such as giraffes in a restricted area but this would not be possible to do with, for example, ants in the same restricted area. The numbers of trees in a forest are relatively easy to count because they don't move!

Samples must be:

- completely random to avoid any bias
- truly representative of the whole area being studied.

To enhance the reliability of the results, many samples must be taken, not just a few.

Using better apparatus will improve the accuracy but not the reliability of the results.

Suppose a student wanted to estimate the average height of male students in first-year at her school using a hand-held measuring tape. If she measures

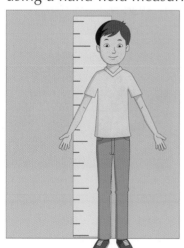

only 5 students out of the total population of 150, this will not be very reliable as she may have 5 students who are all unusually tall. By increasing her sample size, her results become increasingly more reliable. If she changed the tape for a digital height measurer, this would make each individual result more accurate but not necessarily make her overall results any more reliable.

TOP TIP

Don't confuse reliability with accuracy. **R**eliability is obtained with **R**epetition while **A**ccuracy is linked to using better **A**pparatus. Think 'R and R' and 'A and A'.

Evaluating limitations and sources of error in sampling techniques

Any one technique used in ecology will have its own limitations and sources of error, which is why ecologists use a number of different strategies in their studies. Consider two techniques mentioned above, the pitfall trap and quadrat. Here are some of the limitations and sources of error, as well as suggestions as to how the effect of these can be reduced.

TOP TIP

Think of the other techniques mentioned in a similar way.

Sampling technique	Limitations and error sources	Suggested ways of reducing effects
Pitfall trap	Sample obtained may not be representative of the whole area	Take as many samples as possible from as many traps as possible
	Trapped animals may eat each other	Do not leave the traps for long periods before emptying
	Animals may avoid the trap	Ensure it is well blended in with the natural habitat
	Other, larger animals may dip into the trap and eat the small animals	Make sure the trap is suitably covered with a protective lid or stone
Quadrat	Sample obtained may not be representative of the whole area	Take as many samples as possible from as many quadrats as possible
	Some organisms may fall partially in or out of the quadrat	Ensure the method of counting organisms in or out is established and consistently applied to each square
	Samples may not be random	Use some way of ensuring the quadrats are not 'placed' in any patterned way

Measuring abiotic factors

TOP TIP

Remember always to use the phrase 'light intensity' not just 'light' when describing this abiotic factor.

Measuring abiotic factors is a vital part of building up a picture of how an ecosystem is working.

Light meters can be used to measure light intensity.

They are usually placed on the ground and a reading taken from a scale. It is important to give the meter a little time to stabilise and also ensure no accidental shading takes place. The readings should be taken, as far as possible, at the same time to avoid the effects of passing clouds over one site.

Combined meters measure soil water content and pH. They have an electronic probe that is pushed into the soil. It is important to push the probe into the same depth each time (usually there is a special mark to aid this) and it must be cleaned between readings. The meters need time to stabilise before readings are started.

A number of different types of thermometers, including some digital devices, measure air, soil and water temperatures accurately. The meters require time to stabilise between readings and, if a probe is attached, it must be pushed in to the same depth each time and cleaned between readings.

TOP TIP

Think why the probe needs to be cleaned between readings.

Meters now can easily be attached to software to capture data over a period of time and link up with a computer. As with all measurements, repeated sampling is required to ensure reliable results.

To identify animals and plants studied in ecosystems, biologists use devices called **keys**. The most common type of key uses statements arranged in pairs. The paired statements usually give some feature that may or may not be present leading on to more statements and ultimately naming the plant or animal.

1.	Wings present	Bee
	Wings absent	Go to 2
2.	Eight legs	House spider
	Six legs	Go to 3
3.	Narrow waist	Ant
	Broad waist	Flea

Quick Test

1. A student decided to study the invertebrates living on the branches and leaves of a chestnut tree and an elder tree. He used the method shown.

   (a) Would his results be representative of all the different kinds of invertebrates living on this tree? Explain your answer.

   (b) State two variables he would need to ensure he kept the same throughout to make his comparison between the trees valid.

2. Give a named technique that might be used to measure an abiotic factor. For this technique, identify one possible source of error and state how this error might be minimised.

3. What is a biological key used for?

Adaptation, natural selection and the evolution of species

Mutations

Occasionally a change can occur in the genetic make-up of an organism. This is called a **mutation**. Mutations are random, spontaneous events and in no way directed. They can occur anywhere in the genetic material of an organism's cells affecting that organism only. However, if mutations occur in the reproductive cells, the effect can be passed on to the next generation. Variations between individuals rely on mutations.

Mutations that have no effect on the organism are called **neutral**. Sometimes the effect may be positive and give some kind of advantage; if negative it gives some kind of disadvantage to the organism.

The natural rate of mutations can be increased by environmental factors such as radiation and chemicals. Any agent that increases mutation rates is called a **mutagen**. Mutagens include:

- ultraviolet light
- X-rays
- gamma rays
- tars in cigarette smoke
- mustard gas.

Some viruses are known to induce mutations.

TOP TIP

If a mutation is advantageous, the organism is more likely to survive and pass on this mutated gene to the next generation.

Radiation

UV radiation
both natural sunlight and tanning beds

X-Rays
medical, dental, airport security screening

Chemicals

Cigarette smoke
contains dozens of mutagenic chemicals

Benzoyl peroxide
common ingredient in acne products

Nitrate and nitrate preservatives
in hot dogs and other processed meats

Barbecuing
creates mutagenic chemicals in foods

Infectious agents

Human Papillomavirus (HPV)
sexually transmitted virus

Helicobacter pylori
bacteria spread through contaminated food

Variation within a population

Mutations are the basic cause of the variations that exist within and between species. Over a long period of time, often millions of years, inheritable variations allow organisms to change, or evolve, to meet different environmental conditions. This is why organisms often seem so well adapted to suit their particular habitat.

The desert rat is perfectly adapted for desert life. The colour of its fur blends in magnificently with its surroundings. Desert rats can survive without ever drinking natural water, obtaining the moisture they need from their food during respiration. They have large eyes and good vision. Their hearing is so acute, they can pick up the sound of an approaching owl. Their muscular large back legs allow them to jump up to nearly 3 m to escape predators!

Some orchids and moths have evolved together. The moths depend on the orchids to supply them with nectar, while the flowers depend on the moths to spread their pollen for reproduction. The moth has evolved a very long mouthpart that enables it to penetrate deeply into the orchid to obtain the nectar. As the moth sucks up the nectar, pollen sticks to its body. When the moth visits another orchid to feed, the pollen rubs off its body and pollinates the orchid.

The acacia tree has huge, hollow thorns that are ideal homes for ants. It also provides the ants with a ready source of food in the form of nectar and protein from specialised small structures that develop on the acacia leaves. The acacia benefits by having very aggressive guardians that ward off potential herbivores with their very strong sting.

TOP TIP

Investigate other examples of adaptations such as the effects of overuse of antibiotics.

Natural selection

The gradual development of organisms over very long periods of time is known as **evolution**. A theory of evolution was put forward by Charles Darwin in the 19ᵗʰ century. He made a number of observations, based on much research and data collected over years, then formed conclusions based on those observations.

Charles Darwin.

Observations	Organisms are capable of producing many more offspring than can ever survive or the environment can support
	Generally populations of organisms tend to remain the same size over periods of time
Conclusion	Not all the offspring survive; many must die before being able to reproduce
Observation	Variations exist in populations of a species and these variations may be inheritable
Conclusions	Offspring that, by chance, possess some inheritable enhanced features that give them an advantage over other members of the population are more liable to survive and reproduce
	In surviving to reproduce, the organisms in turn pass on those same desirable features to their offspring
	Eventually, those organisms with the desirable features will dominate, perhaps to the point of eliminating other organisms that do not possess those same features
	With the passing of time, new species can evolve

The formation of a new species is called **speciation**.

One of the best examples of evolution in action is the peppered moth. It exists in two different forms; one that is brightly coloured and one that is black. This difference in phenotype is genetically based. Before the Industrial Revolution in the late 18ᵗʰ century the brightly coloured form was the most common. Its colour allowed it to blend in well against the barks of trees. The black coloured one only appeared rarely as a mutated form and was spotted and eaten quickly by birds. However, due to the increase in air pollution during the Industrial Revolution, tree barks became

TOP TIP

Evolution is usually a very gradual process which takes place over millions of years.

increasingly darkened by soot giving the black moths the advantage over the brightly coloured forms. The black forms soon became the most common form because birds couldn't see them against the dark tree barks. By the middle of the 20th century, in polluted areas the black form dominated but in non-polluted areas the brightly coloured form was the most common.

As air quality has improved dramatically in recent years the black forms are once again rarely found.

> **TOP TIP**
>
> This is an example of 'high speed' evolution in action and can also be seen in the development of antibiotic-resistant strains of bacteria.

Speciation

The numbers and types of different species on Earth continue to change as some species become extinct and new species arise. The formation of species needs a change in the gene pool of a population usually as a result of some barrier that causes smaller groups to form. These smaller groups are then somehow prevented from interbreeding. This is called **isolation**. Each sub-population will continue to breed independently of the others with variations arising due to mutations. These variations will be different in each sub-population. The effect of natural selection on those variations will not be the same due to different environmental conditions. This means changes will increase until eventually the sub-populations are no longer able to interbreed, should the barriers be removed. At this point, the sub-populations would be termed new species.

> **TOP TIP**
>
> These changes take place over vast periods of time.

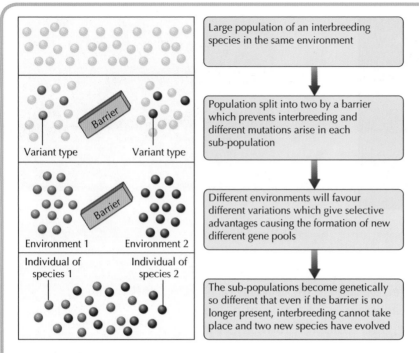

Large population of an interbreeding species in the same environment

↓

Population split into two by a barrier which prevents interbreeding and different mutations arise in each sub-population

↓

Different environments will favour different variations which give selective advantages causing the formation of new different gene pools

↓

The sub-populations become genetically so different that even if the barrier is no longer present, interbreeding cannot take place and two new species have evolved

There are several different ways in which barriers to gene transfer can be set up:

- ecological
- reproductive
- geographical.

Ecological barriers include changes in environmental conditions such as increasing or decreasing temperature, humidity levels, pH and water availability, which can produce localised areas that are unsuitable for a population, thereby splitting it into one or more sub-populations.

Reproductive barriers occur when sub-populations become sexually active at different times, fail to display attractive behaviour patterns, develop incompatible sexual organs or pollination mechanisms no longer function.

Geographical barriers are physical in nature such as rivers, oceans, mountains and deserts, which prevent sub-populations exchanging genes.

The Isle of Arran is home to two of Scotland's rarest tree species: the Arran whitebeam and the Arran cut-leaved whitebeam. They are located in two glens that have different environmental conditions of altitude, which may have been an ecological barrier in the past, separating a single species into two sub-populations that eventually became two new species.

TOP TIP

Remember the sub-populations formed by barriers must acquire different mutations to allow different variations to arise.

Quick Test

1. 'A mutation is a change in an organism's genotype directed by a change in the environment.' Is this statement true or false? Explain your answer.

2. Give three ways in which the desert rat minimises water loss.

3. The brightly coloured and black coloured forms of the peppered moth are variations within the same species. How could you prove this?

Human impact on the environment

Increasing human population

A stable environment can only support a certain number of a particular organism, called the **carrying capacity**. For most species, the carrying capacity remains constant with time. As adults die they are replaced by offspring, not all of which survive.

A number of factors keep the population in check such as:

- food and water availability
- numbers of predators
- disease
- competition.

The concept of carrying capacity applies also to humans. Present estimates of the human population put the number at around 7·5 billion people with this potentially rising to over 9 billion by 2050. We are not subject to the same regulatory factors as other species because we can control their impact. For example, humans no longer are subject to animal predation!

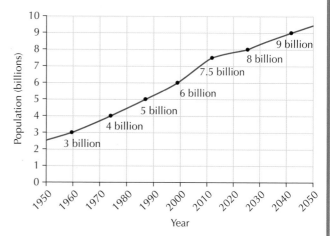

The huge increase in the human population continues to require more efficient ways of producing food to meet the demand. Early humans were **hunter-gatherers**, moving around to find food where and when it was available. With the development of agriculture and permanent settlements came increasing social interaction and stability. The effect of this was to increase the carrying capacity of the environment; the population increased but not dramatically.

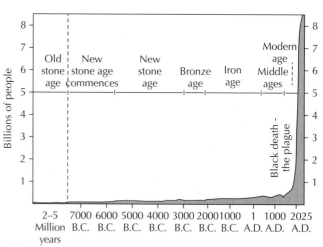

Only since the 1600s, has the population number shown a dramatic rise.

In 2009 the United Nations claimed it would be necessary to increase food production by over 70% over the next 40 years to feed the world's increasing population. Humans have been able to meet the food demands of an increasing population by a number of combined strategies such as:

- Genetic diversity: growing a variety of different strains of crops that have similar features but originate from different parents. Such plants can be bred to increase yields and have natural resistance to pests and diseases. Genetic diversity is important in cattle and fish breeding programmes. Increased yields in animal food production and their products, such as milk, has made huge strides forward over the past 30 years or so.

- Improvement in soil activity: addition of organic material will encourage a wider variety of different organisms, increasing biodiversity. A wider range of plants will grow on such nutrient-rich soils. Rotating crops will prevent the build-up of specific pests. Keeping soils well aerated prevents anaerobic conditions developing and improves water drainage.

- Employing modern farming techniques: use of knowledge-based strategies for obtaining a more realistic potential for land used to grow crops; using the best balance of feed for animals to obtain the highest yield.

- Use of genetically modified organisms: animals and plants can be genetically modified to increase their yield, make them easier to grow and harvest, be resistant to disease and have increased nutritional profiles.

Algal blooms

Bodies of water such as lakes, reservoirs, rivers and streams will contain plant life which includes **algae**. These are microscopic, photosynthetic organisms that lack the usual structures associated with plants such as stems, roots and leaves. Like any plant, its growth is affected by levels of sunlight, carbon dioxide availability, suitable temperature and nutrients such as phosphorus and nitrogen.

> **TOP TIP**
> Sometimes algal blooms can occur naturally due, for example, to changing weather patterns bringing up nutrients from deep waters.

These nutrients are found as phosphates and nitrates, which, on occasions, can be **leached** by rainwater from soil that has had fertilisers added. If these nutrients find their way into bodies of water, they will cause the algae to multiply rapidly to form an **algal bloom**.

Associated with modern-day farming methods and living styles, there has been an increase in this nutrient loading or **eutrophication** of water. Some causes include:

- leaching of inorganic fertiliser (containing nitrates and phosphates)
- leaching of organic fertiliser manure (containing nitrates and phosphates) from intensive farming
- leaching from erosion (following mining, construction work or poor land use)
- discharge of detergents (containing phosphates)
- discharge of partially treated or untreated sewage (containing nitrates and phosphates).

> **TOP TIP**
> Many supermarkets have withdrawn washing products with high levels of phosphates.

The enhanced growth of the algae (and other aquatic plants) reduces the levels of dissolved oxygen in the water when dead plant material decomposes. The lowered levels of oxygen in turn then affect organisms, such as fish and other aquatic life forms, which may die.

> **TOP TIP**
> On land, excess nutrients can leave the soil and don't cause too much damage, but in bodies of water, such excess nutrients have nowhere to go.

Some algal blooms can pose a threat to land animals including humans. For example, if humans eat fish or shellfish from water polluted by certain toxic algae, they may become ill. Even dogs licking the water from a reservoir with a heavy algal bloom have been known to die. Treated water taken from such reservoirs may not show any colouration but the toxins can still be present. In strong winds, sprays can be set up so that tiny droplets of contaminated water get taken in by birds causing damage to brain, kidneys and liver.

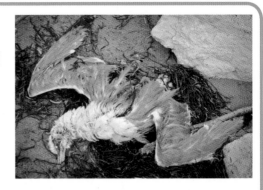

Tourism suffers if bodies of water become unusable for leisure pursuits such as swimming, fishing and sailing. Foul odours associated with algal deaths can make such areas unpleasant to visit.

Lost revenue can be substantial, not just in the context of tourism but also to commercial fishing as well.

Use of pesticides

It is now common practice to grow crops, as single or **monocultures**. An unfortunate consequence of this is that if a pest or disease can attack one of the plants, it can attack all of them. Crops can be infected by viruses, fungi or bacteria, or invaded by invertebrate animals such as insects, slugs and worms. Vertebrates, such as rats, can also become pests if they feed on grain and seeds. Growers may resort to using chemicals called **pesticides** to control pests. The crop yield is thereby increased, reducing costs and making harvesting easier and more efficient.

While strict legislation governs what chemicals can be used and how they are applied, it is still possible that some residual chemicals might be washed into waterways causing pollution. Chemicals can also find their way into food chains, thereby affecting balanced ecosystems. It is nearly impossible to find a pesticide that will target only the pest species without affecting other organisms as well. Past experiences have shown that wildlife and humans can be affected.

TOP TIP

The use of pesticides has been linked with some health problems for humans such as cancer and infertility.

Various governmental agencies in Britain monitor the effect of prolonged use of pesticides and the effect on human health, even in small doses. For example, the chemical vinclozalin is used to control fungal infections such as rotting and moulds in vineyards, orchards on lettuces, beans, peas and onions. It is often also used by the people who manage golf courses. However, research has shown it can affect proper reproductive hormone function in humans. Other anti-fungal agents have been shown to have similar effects on human reproductive function by affecting sperm production and unborn babies.

It is estimated that commercial growers now use only a fraction of the chemicals compared with thirty years ago. Some chemicals that were used freely, such as DDT, are no longer allowed. DDT is one of a number of pesticides that can persist in the environment and bioaccumulate. Since it is very soluble in fat, it can develop high levels in any food that is fatty, such as fish, meat and dairy products. It has been linked to cancer by affecting hormone production in men.

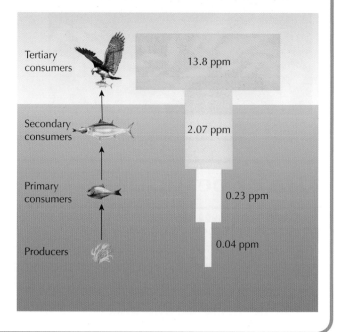

Tertiary consumers — 13.8 ppm
Secondary consumers — 2.07 ppm
Primary consumers — 0.23 ppm
Producers — 0.04 ppm

There is a large group of chemicals called **organophosphates** that forms the basis of many pesticides. They are capable of entering our bodies through the skin, by inhalation into the lungs and by ingestion through contaminated food. A concern is that they can affect enzyme function, particularly associated with proper functioning of the nervous system.

A developing baby's nervous system is very sensitive to such chemicals, which are capable of crossing the placenta. It has been suggested that some behavioural disorders in children might be linked to this route.

The human immune system is very rudimentary in our early life, particularly before birth, and there is a possibility that pesticides might weaken this.

The main concerns are the long-term effects of ingesting chemicals because these may not appear until many years later, as symptoms develop only gradually. This often makes it very difficult to prove cause and effect. While the government sets maximum levels for usage, these long-term effects are still being researched.

> **TOP TIP**
> DDT has been banned in the UK since the 1980s.

Quick Test

1. What is meant by the 'carrying capacity' of an environment?
2. How can genetically modified food help to feed the world's increasing population?
3. Give three causes of eutrophication.

Indicator species

If an ecosystem changes, the organisms that normally live there will be affected. Some organisms are particularly sensitive to even small changes in variables such as pH, temperature, light intensity etc. They may either decrease or increase in numbers.

Lichen is an association between two organisms, an alga and a fungus. It is very sensitive to levels of sulphur dioxide pollution and, in general, will not tolerate even a small rise in such pollution. The numbers and appearance will change considerably if, for example, levels of the gas sulphur dioxide rise. Rock surfaces and tree barks with a dense and healthy lichen growth indicate good air quality.

Otters will not thrive in water that is polluted. They are carnivores and so, if there is pollution in their habitat, they will bioaccumulate any pollutants present in their prey.

Certain maidenhair ferns will only grow in habitats that have a mineral called serpentine. Thus the growth of these ferns indicates the presence of this mineral and a particular type of soil substrate.

Some woodpeckers are found only in well-established and stable woodlands. Large numbers of these birds indicate a good quality habitat. If the health of this animal starts to decline, it is an indication that the ecological health of the habitat is in poor condition for some reason.

Water containing a large number of the early (nymph) stages of stoneflies and mayflies indicates high levels of oxygen in the water. However, if these are found to be absent and bloodworms are present in high numbers, this is a good indication of low levels of oxygen and high levels of pollution, often by sewage.

Organisms such as these, that can indicate the condition of a particular habitat or environment, are called **indicator species**. They are a very powerful monitoring tool for indicating the levels of certain variables and how these levels change over time because they are very sensitive to small increases or decreases in these variables.

TOP TIP

Remember, the indicator species may be absent or present as an index of ecological health.

Biological control

An alternative method of controlling pests is becoming increasingly used. This is called **biological control** because it uses living organisms instead of chemicals. One of its main advantages is being environmentally friendly; it uses naturally occurring organisms rather than potentially harmful chemicals. The main form of this control involves importing known, target-specific predators from another region into the area where the pest organism is located.

Biological control has a number of advantages. It can provide a stable way of regulating the numbers of a pest, thereby improving crop production or saving threatened species.

In the 1950s a virus that causes the disease **myxomatosis** in rabbits was deliberately introduced to control their numbers. The effects were dramatic and within two years, the population had dropped from about 600 million to only 100 million. It was the world's first biological control of a mammalian pest.

Most garden and greenhouse plants are attacked by **aphids**, insects that suck the sap from plants and stunt normal growth. Their numbers can be controlled by introducing a known predator, the ladybird, both in adult and larval forms. One ladybird can eat over 400 000 aphids in its lifetime! However, if the number of aphids is low, the ladybirds can experience a shortage of food and may migrate to other areas or, if they are inside a glasshouse, they will eventually starve to death.

TOP TIP

The biological control organism does not eliminate the pest; it only controls its numbers to an acceptable level.

In some parts of Australia, the *Opuntia* cactus is a pest because of its rapid growth. In the mid 1920s, the only effective control was hazardous chemicals and, at the time, many farmers had to abandon large areas of their land. Now numbers of the cactus are controlled by a special moth that can detect particular chemicals found in this species. The larvae feed on the cactus, destroying it.

However, biological control can also go wrong. It may, for example, affect other species as well as the pest. In the 1950s, a cane toad was introduced into Australia to control a sugar beet beetle. The toad is highly poisonous and has very few predators so it has now become a pest!

A silkworm insect called the gypsy moth caused devastating damage to many trees in North America in the latter part of the 19th century. A fungus was discovered in the late 1980s that infected and killed the moth. The spores of this fungus have been used as a form of biological control in other parts of America.

Biological control organisms work best if they possess the following features. They should:

- ideally, be host specific or target only a very narrow range of hosts; organisms that feed on a wide variety of hosts will not reduce the population of the pest host if other food is available
- be able to tolerate possible new climatic conditions that may be warmer or cooler, drier or wetter than the control organism's normal environment
- kill the pest
- be present when the pest organism's life cycle first starts so that their numbers are checked quickly and effectively
- be easy to work with in a laboratory
- have a good ability to locate the pest organisms
- have a high reproductive potential so that their numbers are adequate to suppress the target pest numbers
- not eliminate the target pest completely or it risks having not enough food to survive itself
- not harm the environment
- remain stable over a long period of time
- be easy to produce in large numbers.

TOP TIP

Biological control is not a 'quick fix' solution because natural predators of a pest can take a long time to reduce the pest population to an acceptable level.

An alternative strategy for controlling pests is to breed resistant varieties of crops. These are known as **genetically modified crops** because their genotypes have been changed to confer an in-built resistance to particular pests.

TOP TIP

You might want to revise the topic of genetic engineering.

The technique for changing the genotype is genetic engineering. As well as engineering pest resistance, scientists have been able to produce plants with other desirable phenotypes, such as increased yields. Thus a given area of farmland can be made to produce more food than previously. This helps to reduce the effects of intensive farming methods. Other enhanced phenotypes might allow plants to tolerate more extreme environmental conditions of temperature, lack of water and low light intensities.

The use of genetic engineering to modify crops has not been without its critics. There is a balance between the benefits and potential dangers that must be met before such a crop is allowed to be grown and ultimately end up in the human food chain.

Rape seed plants can be engineered to resist a particular chemical used to control a pest infestation such as a weed. Farmers can spray the genetically modified crops with that chemical, eliminating the weed without damaging the plant. This means that there will be a much larger yield of the rape seed plant, using a more environmentally-friendly spray to control the pests and less of the spray. However, the genes conferring the resistant phenotype might find their way into other species because the pollen from rape seed plants can also pollinate weeds. In this way, the genes could confer resistance on those weeds which would then be resistant to the chemical.

Sweetcorn can be genetically engineered to produce a poison that kills insect pests. Thus the farmer no longer needs to use any chemical sprays and the potential damage to the environment and other species is eliminated. The yield is also increased. However, this corn will continue to kill the insects for as long as it is growing, which gives rise to the possibility of a natural selection for insects that are resistant. In that case, the poison would no longer be effective. Other desirable insects, such as butterflies, might be killed as well as the target pest.

Scientists have been able to engineer rice so that it makes a chemical that humans can change into vitamin A. This rice therefore becomes a rich source of a vitamin, which is deficient in some diets, especially in under-developed areas. However, people in these areas may become over-dependent on this rice. Since it is often linked with commercial enterprises, the producers ensure that the plants are sterile so that the growers cannot re-plant them and have to buy a new stock each year.

Tomatoes previously had a relatively short shelf-life because they produce a chemical that causes rotting. They can now be engineered to produce less of this chemical and so stay fresher for much longer.

Clearly there are a number of pros and cons to the development of genetically modified crops.

Advantages:

- nutritional content can be enhanced
- taste is improved
- less chemicals need to be used
- money is saved
- the environment is not exposed to potentially harmful pesticides
- crops remain fresher for longer
- higher yields can be obtained
- crops can be transported for a longer time
- harvesting is easier if the crops are ready at the same time.

TOP TIP

You should discuss and investigate the ethical issues surrounding the use of genetically modified crops and food.

Concerns:

- crops that are already genetically engineered to be resistant to antibiotics may pass on the genes conferring resistance to animals and people
- consumers are not always convinced the crops and their products are safe to eat
- other organisms might be affected if animals eat the genetically modified crops
- there might be no way to ensure control of the modified crops, which might spread from where they were initially grown
- genes that have been transferred from nuts into other organisms have caused major health concerns for people with nut allergies
- companies might end up with sole control of genetically modified crops
- the outcome is not always precise and predictable.

Quick Test

1.	What is an 'indicator species'?
2.	Give one advantage and one disadvantage of biological control.
3.	Make up a table of the advantages and concerns about using genetically modified food.

End of Unit Questions

Section A

1. Which of the following is correct?

	Biotic factor	Abiotic factor
A	Length of day	Food supply
B	Altitude	Latitude
C	Competition	Predation
D	Disease	Climate

2. The following diagram represents some of the processes involved in the nitrogen cycle.

Which of the following are the correct descriptions of the bacteria involved?

	1	2
A	Decomposing	Nitrifying
B	Denitrifying	Decomposing
C	Nitrogen fixing	Nitrifying
D	Nitrifying	Denitrifying

3. In an ecological investigation samples should be:

A random and few in number

B representative and random

C many in number and non-random

D small in number and random

4. The graph below represents the number of different fish species found in a variety of lakes of different pHs.

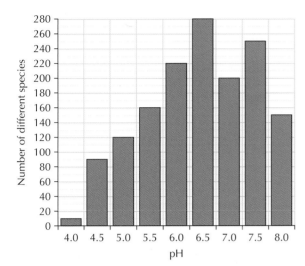

   Which of the following statements is correct?

   A The greatest number of different species is found at pH 4·0.

   B There are more different species at pH 8·0 than at pH 7·0.

   C With increasing pH there is a consistent increase in the number of different species.

   D The largest number of different species is found at pH 6·5.

5. The following statements refer to the events that might lead to an algal bloom in a river:

   1. algae near the surface of the river grow rapidly
   2. fertilisers are added to crops and run off due to excessive rain
   3. nitrate levels in the river rise
   4. algae form a carpet over the surface of the river

   Which is the correct order of events?

   A 1, 2, 3, 4

   B 4, 3, 2, 1

   C 2, 1, 3, 4

   D 2, 3, 1, 4

Section B

1. What term is used to describe specific regions that share similar climates and in which similar animals and plants are found? [1]

2. State three variables that can affect an organism's niche. [1]

3. The following is a simple pyramid of energy:

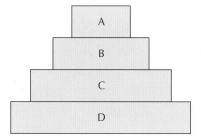

   (a) At which level would photosynthesis be taking place? [1]

   (b) Give two reasons why not all the energy at one level is available to the next level above. [1]

4. What is meant by a pollution indicator species? [1]

5. Plant growth is affected by levels of air pollutants such as sulphur dioxide. A genetically engineered plant that can tolerate high levels of sulphur dioxide was tested by a student in her school laboratory using the apparatus below.

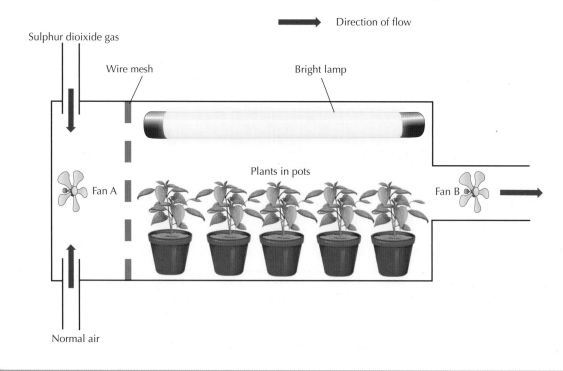

Five samples of the genetically engineered plants were grown in pots and then placed in the chamber. Sulphur dioxide gas was mixed with normal air using a fan to give a known concentration well above the usual atmospheric concentrations of the gas and the mixture was drawn through by a second fan. A bright lamp was kept on throughout the experiment. A similar chamber, with another five genetically engineered plants, was set up as a control using only normal air. After six weeks, the student collected, dried, then weighed all the plant material from both chambers. The results, shown as 'dry mass' are in the following table.

Chamber	Dry mass of each plant (g)					Average dry mass (g)
Experimental with sulphur dioxide gas	12	10	11	12	12	
Control with normal air	18	20	18	21	23	

(a) Copy and complete the table by calculating the average dry mass for each chamber. [1]

(b) In the experimental set up, what was the purpose of each of the following?

  (i)   Wire mesh

  (ii) Bright lamp

  (iii) Fan A

  (iv) Fan B. [4]

(c) State two precautions the student would have to take when measuring the dry mass of each plant. [2]

(d) State three variables that should be kept the same throughout the investigation. [3]

(e) Give an example of a flaw in the design of this investigation and explain how you would attempt to correct it. [2]

(f) How could the student improve the reliability of the results? [1]

(g) The student concluded that the decrease in the average growth rate of the plants in the sulphur dioxide enriched atmosphere was due to an in ability of the plants to photosynthesise properly.

  Was this a valid conclusion? Explain your answer. [2]

Glossary

abiotic factor
any condition affecting the environment that results from non-living sources

absorption
process by which small, soluble molecules are taken up by cells

active site
area on an enzyme's surface that binds with a specific substrate

active transport
energy-demanding process in cells that moves substances against a concentration gradient

adenine
base that is one of three chemicals making up a nucleotide

adenosine diphosphate
molecule similar to ATP with one less phosphate group

adenosine triphosphate (ATP)
molecule that is the main energy carrier molecule in cells

aerobic respiration
type of respiration requiring oxygen in which substrates such as glucose are completely broken down to water and carbon dioxide to release large amounts of energy

agar
chemical obtained from seaweed that causes a liquid to set hard

albinism
genetically determined condition that results in none of the normal pigment found in hair, skin and eyes

alga
simple one-celled or many-celled plant found mostly in water which uses sunlight to produce its own food

algal bloom
excess algae often associated with an increase in the nutrient level in a body of water

allele
different forms of a gene

alveolus
commonly called an air sac, blind-ending, thin-walled sac where gas exchange takes place in the lungs

amino acid
basic building-block of a protein

amylase
enzyme that breaks starch down into the sugar maltose

anaemia
reduction in the haemoglobin content of the blood that can render the person easily tired and prone to infections

anaerobic respiration
respiration that does not require oxygen

anther
male structure in a flowering plant which produces pollen

antibiotic
chemical produced by a microorganism used to kill or inhibit the growth of bacteria

antibody
large protein molecule produced in response to invasion by a foreign agent and capable of rendering it harmless

aorta
large artery taking blood rich in oxygen from the heart

aphid
sap-sucking insect that stunts the growth of plants it infects

apical meristem
region of actively dividing cells at the tip of the stem or root

artery
vessel carrying blood to the heart

aseptic technique
any process that prevents contamination of the environment by the culture being used and also that prevents the environment contaminating the culture

116

atheroma
fatty mass deposited on the walls of arteries

atrium
upper thin-walled chamber of the heart that receives blood from the body or the lungs

bacterium
microscopic one-celled organism with no nucleus but with a definite cell wall and plasmids

base
nitrogen-containing chemical such as adenine, thymine, cytosine, guanine or uracil that forms part of a nucleotide

bioaccumulation
increase in concentration of a substance in living material due to the inability to break down and/or excrete this substance

biodiversity
all the different species that live in an environment

biological control
method of controlling pests using naturally occurring living organisms to regulate the size of the pest population

biomass
total mass of living things in an environment expressed as the dry mass

biome
major area in the environment defined by its climate, flora and fauna

biosphere
part of the Earth's surface and atmosphere within which life can exist

biotic factor
anything that affects the environment as a result of the activities of living things

bone marrow
tissue found inside bones which manufactures blood cells

brain
complex of nerve cells found inside the skull where all the higher level activities take place

bronchiole
small division of the bronchus found deep within the lungs

bronchitis
inflammation of the bronchi

bronchus
division of the windpipe (trachea) that carries air into the lungs from the mouth

capillary
smallest diameter blood vessel whose walls are only one cell thick and across which exchange of gases, nutrients and wastes takes place

carbohydrate
chemical containing the elements carbon, hydrogen and oxygen

carbon fixation
combination, by photosynthetic plants, of the gas carbon dioxide with hydrogen to produce glucose

carrying capacity
maximum number of any one species that can be sustained over time in a particular habitat

cartilage
collection of cells with a tough "plastic" texture

catalyst
chemical that can speed up a reaction

cell culture
growing cells in the laboratory, outside of a living organism

cell membrane
outer covering of cells that regulates what can enter or leave

cell wall
relatively thick layer found on the outside of plant, fungal and bacterial cells. In each case, it is chemically different but functions to give the cell shape and helps protect internal cell structures

cellulose
main structural chemical that makes up plant cell walls

central nervous system
consists of brain and spinal cord

centromere
area of a chromosome where the chromatids are held together

Glossary

cerebellum
part of the brain associated with balance and co-ordinating voluntary muscle activity

cerebral hemisphere
one of a pair of large lobes that form the cerebrum

cerebrum
largest part of the brain occupying space from above eyes to back of the head

cervix
muscular ring at the neck of the uterus leading into the vagina

chamber
in the heart, one of the four cavities that collect and discharge blood

chitin
chemical found in the cell walls of fungi consisting of millions of strands of cellulose interwoven

chlorophyll
green pigment found in chloroplasts capable of trapping light energy

chloroplast
structure found in green plant cells that contains the pigment chlorophyll and where photosynthesis takes place

chromatid
one of two identical strands forming a chromosome

chromosome complement
total number and types of chromosomes found in the nucleus of a cell

chromosome
thread-like structure composed of deoxyribonucleic acid found in the nucleus and carrying genetic instructions

cilium
small threadlike structure that extends from the surface of a cell. It lines a body part such as the trachea and can move in a rhythmic and co-ordinated way

circulatory system
collective name for the blood, vessels and heart

collagen
important chemical found in bone and skin that gives strength

community
collection of animals and plants living together in a particular habitat

complementary base pairing
linking of bases by hydrogen bonding in specific combinations

concentration gradient
difference in the concentration of substances from one area to another

continuous variation
continual spread across a sample of a population for variables that are often controlled by a number of factors

cuticle
continuous waxy layer that covers the surfaces exposed to the air

cytoplasm
watery substance found inside cells where all the chemical reactions of the cell take place

cytosine
base that is one of three chemicals making up a nucleotide

decomposer
any living thing that can break down dead material to allow nutrients to be recycled in ecosystems

denaturation
irreversible change in a protein, caused by changes in pH or temperature, that renders the activity of an enzyme useless

denitrifying bacteria
organisms that are capable of breaking down nitrate and releasing nitrogen into the atmosphere

deoxyribonucleic acid (DNA)
complex, helically-shaped molecule of heredity within which are encoded instructions for constructing, controlling and reproducing cells by determining the synthesis of proteins

deoxyribose
5-carbon sugar found in DNA

diabetes
disorder that results in the inability to control blood glucose levels, commonly associated with lack of insulin

diaphragm
strong sheet of muscle separating the chest cavity from the lower gut cavity and is important in breathing

diffusion
sometimes referred to as passive transport, is the movement of substances from an area of high concentration to an area of low concentration without the use of energy

diploid number
total number of chromosomes in the nucleus

discontinuous variation
another name for discontuous variation

discrete variation
differences in a particular feature fall into distinct categories and cannot be easily measured

dominant allele
form of a gene that masks the effect of the recessive form of the allele and produces a dominant phenotype

double helix
the characteristic shape of the DNA molecule which consists of two strands, each of which turns regularly about itself to form a cylindrical shape held together by weak hydrogen bonds

ecological barrier
means by which a species becomes divided into two or more sub-groups based on some change in the environment

ecosystem
complex community of different species of animals and plants that are dependent on each other and the environment

effector
structure that brings about an action as a result of an input from a nerve pathway

egg
female sex cell

electron microscope
microscope that does not use visible light to illuminate an object for viewing and is capable of very high magnification and great detail

embryo
in animals developmental stage from foetal stage up to time of birth

emphysema
disease of the lungs where the walls of the alveoli become progressively reduced leading to a much reduced surface area for gas exchange

endocrine gland
collection of cells that produce and release chemicals directly into the bloodstream

endocrine system
collection of glands that release chemicals directly into the bloodstream

enzyme
protein that has the ability to cause a reaction in a living cell to take place quickly when it would otherwise take place slowly or not at all

epidermis
in a multicellular organism the outer layer of cells, usually one cell thick in plants

equator
plane of cell along which chromosomes line up during mitosis

ethanol
an alcohol produced during anaerobic respiration by plant cells

eutrophication
general term for the loading of a body of water with nutrients

evolution
process by which living things have gradually changed over a very long period of time to become better suited to survive and reproduce in their environment

family tree
pictorial representation of a family's inheritance patterns over a number of generations

fat
chemical, usually solid at room temperature, used as an energy-store

fatty acid
chemical that, when combined with glycerol, forms fat molecules

fauna
collective name for the animals in a particular environment

Glossary

fermentation

type of anaerobic respiration found in plant and yeast cells that results in the production of ethanol, carbon dioxide and small quantities of ATP

fermenter

device used to grow cells in large quantities very rapidly under carefully controlled conditions

fertilization

fusion of male and female gametes to form a zygote

first filial generation

offspring produced as a result of a parental cross

flora

general term for the plant life in a particular environment

foetus

young animal in its early stages of development and still within the mother's uterus

fungus

organism that has no chlorophyll, has a cell wall made of chitin and often feeds on dead animal or plant materials

gamete

sex cell that possess half the diploid number of chromosomes

gene

basic unit of heredity which corresponds to a length of DNA

genetic counselling

information given to people on the nature of conditions that are inherited

genetic engineering

term for different techniques to deliberately alter the DNA of a cell by inserting part or all of the genetic material from another cell which may or may not be from the same species of organism

genetically modified crops

plants whose DNA has been changed by genetic engineering

genetically modified

description of a cell's genetic material after it has been changed by genetic engineering

genotype

the combination of the alleles of a gene or genes

geographical barrier

means by which a species becomes divided into two or more sub-groups based on some major physical obstacle that prevents the sub-groups from continuing to interbreed

gland

organ producing a chemical that brings about a response in any body part which is sensitive to that chemical

glucagon

hormone produced by the pancreas that causes glycogen to be converted to glucose

glucose

simple 6-carbon sugar that is a product of photosynthesis and is used up in respiration

glycerol

a basic component of fat molecules

glycogen

main sugar made up of many glucose molecules and stored in the liver

gonad

ovary or testis of an organism

guanine

base that is one of three chemicals making up a nucleotide

guard cell

specialised cell that surrounds a stoma and regulates the size of the opening

habitat

general term for the place in the an environment where an organism lives

haemoglobin

protein that combines loosely with oxygen in the lungs and then off-loads this in respiring tissues

haploid number

number of chromosomes present in a sex cell

heart

muscular pump situated in the chest cavity behind the breastbone

heavy metal
chemical element that is many times denser than water and has an atomic number greater than 20

heterozygote
an individual with different alleles of the same gene

homozygote
an individual with identical alleles of the same gene

hormone
chemical produced by one part of a plant or animal and transported to target areas to affect function and/ or structure

hunter-gatherer
early human whose survival depended on hunting animals and gathering plants

hydrogen bond
weak force which is responsible for much of the 3-D shape of biological molecules such as proteins and nucleic acids

impulse
of nerves, the message conducted along a nerve

indicator species
organism whose presence or absence indicates the condition of a habitat

inheritance
how characteristics in living things are passed from one generation to another

insulin
hormone that regulates the blood glucose levels by converting glucose to glycogen

interspecific competition
competition between organisms of different species for the same resources

intraspecific competition
competition within organisms of the same species for the same resources

isolation
when a population is split into two or more smaller groups that are prevented from genetic exchange

keratin
structural protein that is the main component of nail, hair and skin

key
system for identification based on observable features, present or absent, of organisms

lacteal
central structure found in each villus that absorbs digested fats

lactic acid
compound formed in animal cells as an end-product of anaerobic respiration during activities which have a high oxygen-demand

lateral meristem
growth area in the stem of a plant whose activity causes an increase in the width of a stem

leaching
process by which dissolved substances, such as phosphates and nitrates in the soil, are washed out by rainwater

lichen
fungi and algae growing together with fungus making up almost 90% of the mass of the combination

lignin
substance found in the xylem of some plant cell walls that it stiffens, helping to stop infection and decay and making the xylem strong

limiting factor
variable that, when increased or decreased, speeds up or slow down a reaction or process

lipid
fat molecule

lymph
typically clear fluid found in the lymphatic system but turns milky when it is carrying digested fats

lymphatic system
system of vessels that, among other functions, transports digested fats from the small intestine

maltose
sugar consisting of two glucose molecules joined together

medulla
part of brain which connects with spinal cord and controls activities that animals are not consciously aware of

Glossary

meristem
area of a plant that is actively dividing found at root and shoot tips as well as stems

messenger ribonucleic acid
chemical that is important in the manufacture of proteins carrying information from the DNA in the nucleus to the ribosomes in the cytoplasm

micron
unit of measurement for cells where 1 mm is equal to 1000 microns

mitochondrion
cylindrically-shaped structure found in varying numbers in the cytoplasm of cells that is the site of aerobic respiration producing adenosine triphosphate (ATP)

mitosis
type of nuclear division that results in the formation of two new cells that share the same genetic instructions as each other and the original cell from which they arose

monoculture
agricultural process in which one crop is grown to the exclusion of all others

monogenic
describing an inherited feature controlled by one gene

motor neuron
nerve cell carrying information towards an effector

mucus
sticky material produced by lining surfaces of body cavities such as the mouth and digestive system often acting as a lubricant

multicellular
describing an organism whose body is made up of many cells

mutagen
general term for any agent that can induce a change in the DNA that does not necessarily result in the death of the cells concerned

mutation
change in the genetic makeup of a cell that can result in an altered phenotype producing a new allele if a gene is affected or a change in the number of the chromosomes

myxomatosis
deadly viral infection of rabbits

natural selection
mechanism by which gradual evolutionary changes take place

nervous system
collection of structures that allows a multicellular animal to coordinate its activities very rapidly

neuron
nerve cell

neutral mutation
change in the genetic makeup of a cell that has no effect on the organism

niche
role played by a particular organism in the environment that is usually a function of the food eaten and a range of variables tolerated

nicotine
chemical derived from tobacco leaves

nitrifying bacteria
convert ammonia to nitrates

nitrogen fixing bacteria
organisms that are capable of trapping atmospheric nitrogen and converting it into nitrate

nucleotide
building unit of nucleic acids that consists of a nitrogen-containing base, 5-carbon sugar and a phosphate groupin

nucleus
controls all the activities of a cell and contains the genetic material

oesophagus
tube connecting mouth to stomach along which food passes

oil
fat which is liquid at room temperature

optimum
value of a factor, such as pH or temperature, at which an enzymes works best

organ
functional unit in a multicellular organism which carries out a specific job

organophosphate
carbon compound which also contains phosphate and is the basis of many pesticides

osmosis
movement of water from an area of high water concentration to an area of low water concentration across a selectively permeable membrane

ovary
organ in which female sex cells are produced in animals and plants

oviduct
tube that carries egg from ovary towards the uterus

ovule
contains the female gamete in plants

ovum
female gamete found in animals

palisade cell
cell that forms a layer between the upper and lower epidermis of a leaf, shaped tall and columnar, and where photosynthesis mainly takes place in a leaf

pancreas
organ associated with the digestive system producing important enzymes and the hormones insulin and glucagon

parental generation
two parents that produce offspring

passive transport
movement of substances from an area of high concentration to an area of low concentration without the use of energy

pesticide
chemical used to kill pests

phenotype
expression of the genes possessed by an individual that is usually a combination of the effects of the genes and the environment

phloem
plant structure that moves food material made in the leaves by photosynthesis to other parts of the plant

photosynthesis
process by which green plant cells use the energy of the sun to combine carbon dioxide and water to form carbohydrate

pigment
coloured compound produced by a living cell

pitfall trap
usually a jar or tin can sunk into the ground into which animals fall and are trapped

plasmid
small circular piece of genetic material commonly found in bacteria and usually made of deoxyribonucleic acid (DNA) that can reproduce independently of the main genetic material

plasmolysed
of plant cells, the condition of excessive water loss

pollen grain
contains the male gamete in plants

pollen tube
narrow structure down which the male gamete travels towards the ovule

pollution
environmental contamination by any substance or unwanted energy

polygenic
description of an inherited feature controlled by more than one gene

pooter
chamber with two tubes attached, one of which is put into the mouth and sucked through while the other draws a small invertebrates into the chamber for later examination

population
group of living things that belong to the same species and live in the same area of the environment

product
end result of an enzyme-catalysed reaction

pulmonary artery
vessel carrying blood low in oxygen from the right ventricle to the lungs

pulmonary vein
vessel carrying blood rich in oxygen from the lungs to the left atrium

Punnett square
simple table to show all possible results from a genetic cross

Glossary

pyramid of biomass
graphical representation of the mass of living things measured at each feeding level in an ecosystem

pyramid of energy
graphical representation showing the energy stored at each feeding level in an ecosystem

pyramid of numbers
graphical representation of the total number of living things at each feeding level in an ecosystem

pyruvate
important 3-C molecule that is an intermediate in respiration

receptor
cell or group of cells that responds to a specific stimulus

receptor
group of molecules on a cell membrane that fits another complementary molecule so that when the two link up, a change in cell function takes place

recessive allele
form of a gene that needs another similar allele for the recessive phenotype to be expressed

red blood cell
cell that has no nucleus and contains the protein haemoglobin to carry oxygen

reflex action
action not usually requiring the brain to be involved and is therefore unconscious

reflex arc
simple nerve pathway connecting a receptor and effector resulting in a specific response to a specific stimulus

relay neuron
nerve cell carrying information from sensory neurone to motor neurone

reproductive barrier
means by which a species becomes divided into two or more sub-groups because they are incompatible in some way or the offspring produced are not fertile

respiration
process by which energy-rich molecules are progressively broken down by enzymes to form adenosine triphosphate

ribosome
small particle which is the site of protein synthesis in a cell

root hair cell
cell found in the root of a plant that has a very large surface area for absorbing water and dissolved solutes

root nodule
small swelling on the roots of some plants that contains bacteria capable of fixing atmospheric nitrogen and converting it into a form that the plant can use as a nutrient

sampling
technique of counting small numbers of a variable as a way of representing the actual number

second filial generation
offspring produced as a result of crossing two members of the first filial generation

selectively permeable
describes how a cell membrane exerts control on the substances that can pass across it

sensory neuron
nerve cell carrying information from a receptor to the central nervous system

sensory receptor
specialised cell or cells that detect stimuli and relay these to the central nervous system

sex cell
gamete or haploid reproductive cell

small intestine
narrow tube about seven metres long starting at the stomach where digestion is completed and absorption takes place

specialisation
when describing a cell, the state of being dedicated to one particular function

speciation
formation of two or more groups of organisms that can no longer interbreed to form fertile offspring

species
group of individuals which can breed together to produce offspring that themselves can reproduce

sperm duct
tube carrying sperms from testes to outside via the penis

sperm
male sex cell which contains half the normal number of chromosomes

spinal column
series of small bones stacked on top of each other that form a tube within which the spinal cord is protected

spinal cord
thick cable-like structure that carries information to and from the brain

spindle
network of fibres that appear during mitosis and move chromosomes within the cell

spongy mesophyll layer
cells that are irregularly shaped found between the upper and lower epidermis creating a large surface area and many air spaces within a leaf

starch
molecule made up of many glucose units joined together

stem cell
cell that is capable of growing into many different types of cell found in the adult animal or plant

stimulus
energy event in the environment or inside an animal's body that can be detected and potentially produce a response

stoma
small opening on the surface of leaves and stems that allows exchange of materials between the environment and the plant

structural protein
long chain of amino acids used as part of the fabric of a cell such as part of the membrane

substrate
chemical on which an enzyme acts

synapse
microscopic space between neurons

target tissue
collection of cells that are sensitive to a hormone

territory
specific area in an environment which is inhabited by one species that will not allow members of the same species to share it and that is defended by the resident member

testis
organ in male animal where sperm are produced

thymine
base that is one of three chemicals making up a nucleotide

tissue
collection of similar cells that perform a specific task

trachea
commonly called the windpipe, the main air passage from the mouth and nose connecting to the lungs via the bronchi and bronchioles

transect line
method of examining part of an ecosystem at regular intervals to look at changes that may occur along a line

transformed
of a cell, the incorporation of genetic material from another organism

transpiration
evaporative loss of water through the surfaces of a land plant

transpiration stream
movement of water through a plant from the roots to the leaves

tree beating
striking a tree branch to cause small animals to fall into a collecting tray held underneath

Tullgren funnel
device for collection of soil invertebrates that move away from a heat/light source into a collecting container

turgid
condition of a plant cell that is full of water

ultrastructure
fine detail of a cell as revealed by the electron microscope

uterus
muscular organ in which the embryo develops

Glossary

vacuole
membrane-bound sac found in plant cells containing a watery solution giving support

vagina
muscular tube that receives the erect penis during sexual reproduction and through which the baby passes during birth

valve
structure that allows movement of contents of a vessel or blood in the heart to flow in one direction only

variable
quantity that can continually increase or decrease

variation
difference which exists between living things that may be a function of the genetic makeup or the environment or a combination of both

vector
in genetic engineering, an agent that can move genes from one species into a different species

vein
vessel carrying blood away from the heart

vena cava
large vein returning blood low in oxygen to the right atrium of the heart

ventricle
thick-walled chamber of the heart that sends blood to the lungs or to the body

vessel
in mammals any tube that carries fluid such as blood

villus
finger-like projection lining the small intestine increasing the surface area available for absorption

voluntary muscle
muscle whose activity is under conscious control

xylem
group of plant cells that transport water and dissolved solutes from the roots to the leaves

yeast
general term for a fungus that exists as a single-celled organism

zygote
fertilized egg at the one-cell stage that contains a full set of chromosomes

got it?

Answers to Quick Tests

Cell structure

1. Plant cell wall is made of cellulose, yeast cell wall is made of chitin

2. Ribosomes and mitochondria

3. Cell wall, nucleus, cytoplasm, cell membrane, ribosomes, mitochondria, vacuole

---

Transport across cell membranes

1. Only certain substances can pass across

2. Oxygen, carbon dioxide, water, amino acids, glucose etc.

3. Active transport is energy-demanding, diffusion does not require energy and active transport moves substances against the concentration gradient, whereas diffusion moves substances down the concentration gradient

---

Producing new cells

1. To ensure there is no loss of genetic material

2. 4

3. Centromere

DNA and the production of proteins

1. Deoxyribose, phosphate and base

2. Adenine - thymine / cytosine – guanine or A-T / C-G

3. Made of protein / not used up in chemical reactions they catalyse / act as catalysts / substrate specific

Proteins and enzymes

1. Determines the shape, type and function of the protein

2. Enzymes are specific for the substrate on which they act / active site of enzyme is complementary to only one substrate

3. When foods break down, the process is enzyme-based; low temperatures will slow down the activity of the enzymes involved in this process

Genetic engineering

1. Basic unit of heredity that corresponds to a definite section of a DNA molecule

2. Long-term effects are not known; altered genes may find their way into other species with unknown consequences

3. Plasmid / virus

Photosynthesis

1. Combination of carbon dioxide and water to produce carbohydrate/sugar/ glucose

2. To supply energy for the plant; converted into starch/cellulose/protein/fats and oils

3. Something that can affect quantity of a product formed / rate of a reaction when it is in short supply

Respiration

1. Allows energy to be released in a controlled way / prevents damage to cells by too much energy being released at once

2. Glucose

3. Glucose + oxygen $\rightarrow$ carbon dioxide + water + energy/ATP

Cells, tissues and organs

1. Multicellular
2. Tissue
3. Organ

Stem cells and meristems

1. (i) Is not yet committed to be a particular type of cell
   (ii) Can divide repeatedly without limit during an animal's lifetime
   (iii) Divides to form two daughter cells, each of which may remain a stem cell or become another type of specialised cell
2. B
3. Apical meristem is found at the tips of roots and shoots and produces growth upwards or downwards. Lateral meristem is found towards the outside of roots and shoots and produces growth outwards

Control and communication

1. Nervous and endocrine systems
2. Change in the environment that can be detected by an animal or plant
3. Insoluble and does not set up osmosis

Reproduction

1. Sperm cell is much smaller than an egg cell; sperm cell has a tail but an egg cell does not
2. 4
3. Gives rise to genetic variation

Variation and inheritance

1. 3 purple-flowered plants: 1 white-flowered plants

2.

Type of variation	
Continuous	**Discrete**
Height	Eye colour
Weight	Hair colour
Hair length	

3. Inheritance that is controlled by more than one gene

The need for transport: plant transport systems

1. (i) Evaporation of water from the leaves on a hot day keeps a plant cool

   (ii) Transpiration stream draws water up the stem from the roots to keep a constant supply of water available to the leaf cells

   (iii) Dissolved minerals are carried in the transpiration stream to all parts of the plant

2. On a dry day the concentration gradient of water between the leaves and the outside is greater than on a humid day so more water will leave the plant by evaporation on a dry day than a humid day and therefore the rate of water movement in the xylem will be greater

3. Strengthen/support plant

The need for transport: animal transport and exchange systems

1. Oxygen and glucose

2. Sticky mucus traps dust and germs
   Small cilia drive the mucus and trapped materials towards the mouth

3. Conversion of food from large pieces to small pieces

Effects of lifestyle choices on animal transport and exchange systems

1. Chemicals in cigarette smoke can travel across the placenta from the mother to the baby

2. Fatty deposits on walls of arteries; narrows space for blood to travel through and increases risk of clots forming

3. Mental and muscle co-ordination are impaired with alcohol intake, as is the ability to judge distances and speeds

Biodiversity and the distribution of life

1.

Abiotic factor	Biotic factor
Temperature, light intensity, humidity, wind, salinity, soil moisture, space	Predation, disease, food availability

2. Habitat

3. Group of different species that lives together and interacts with each other / several different populations living together

Energy in ecosystems

1. Breakdown dead animals and plants / recycle nutrients

2. Breakdown nitrates to release nitrogen into the air

3. Intraspecific occurs between organisms of the same species for the same resources / interspecific occurs between organisms of different species for the same resources

Sampling techniques and the measurement of abiotic and biotic factors

1. (a) No, since: (any one)

   Some animals may escape by flying away / some animals may be too firmly attached to the tree to be dislodged / branches out of reach are not sampled / some animals may live on other parts of the tree

    (b) (Any two)

        Size/area of sheet / how strongly the student beat the tree / number of times student beat tree / height of branches beaten / size/age of tree / where the tree is growing / what time of the year the investigation was carried out

2. (Several possible answers)

    Measuring light intensity using a light meter / readings may be unstable / give meter time to stabilise before taking readings

3. Device used by biologists to identify organisms

Speciation

1. False because mutations are not directed by the environment but occur randomly

2. (Any three)

    Searching for food mainly at night / having few sweat glands / staying in its burrow during the day / producing little urine, which is highly concentrated

3. Allow black and white moths to breed and see if their offspring can interbreed successfully. If they can, they are from the same species.

Human population, algal blooms, pesticides

1. Maximum number of any one species that can be sustained in a habitat over time

2. Increases yields / easier to grow and harvest / resistant to diseases / better nutritional profiles

3. Leaching of inorganic fertiliser / leaching of organic fertiliser / leaching from erosion / discharge of detergents / discharge of untreated sewage

Indicator species, biological control

1. An organism whose presence or absence is an indication of the condition of a habitat

2. Advantage: can provide a stable way of regulating the numbers of a pest / increasing yield / protecting endangered species

    Disadvantage: may affect organisms other than the target pest / takes a long time / does not fully eradicate the pest / may not be predictable

Answers to End of Unit 1 Questions

Section A

1. D
2. B
3. C
4. B
5. D

Section B

1. (a) 60°C
   (b) 40%
   (c) (i) No.
       (ii) The optimum temperature of 60°C is too high for this to be the body temperature of an animal.

2. (a) 4
   (b) 1
   (c) Identify one single strand of any one of the four chromosomes.

3. (a) (i) Turgid
       (ii) A
   (b) The water concentration is lower inside the cell than outside, so water moves in by osmosis.
       There is no cell wall present in an animal cell, such as a red blood cell, so the cell eventually swells up and bursts.

4. (a) (i) Photosynthesis
       (ii) X hydrogen; Y glucose; Z oxygen
   (b) Chlorophyll

5. (a)

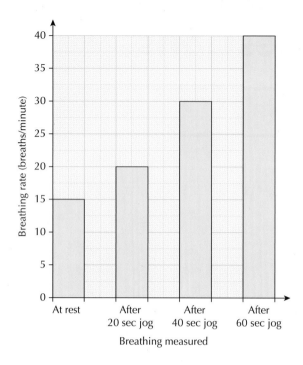

(b) 166·7%

(c) 3: 4: 6: 8

Answers to End of Unit 2 Questions

Section A

1. D
2. D
3. C
4. A
5. B

Section B

1. Connect the terms on the left to the correct statements on the right by means of arrow-headed lines.

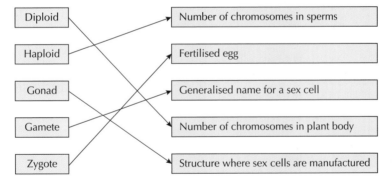

All 5 lines correct for 2 marks; 3 or 4 correct for 1 mark

2. (a) Inheritance controlled by one gene
   (b) Tongue-rolling ability, presence/absence of ear lobes

3. (a) ss x Ss (parents)
      (i)   spotted and plain patterns
      (ii)   Ss and ss
   (b) Ss x Ss (parents)
         1 SS : 2Ss : 1ss

4. xylem ; phloem

135

5.

	Artery	Vein	Capillary
Relative diameter	Small	Large	Small
Wall	Thick muscular	Thin muscular	No muscle
Valves	Present	Absent	Absent

6.

Attempt	Length of lines drawn (cm)		
	Volunteer 1	**Volunteer 2**	**Volunteer 3**
Average (1–5)	7·9	7·7	6·2
Average (6–10)	8·0	7·4	7·2

(a)

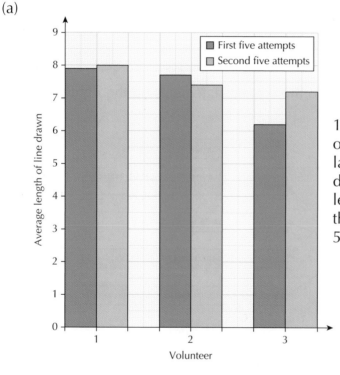

1 mark for correct calculations of averages; 1 mark for correct labelling of axis; 1 mark for drawing bars; 1 mark for leaving equal spaces between the bars and using more than 50% of the grid

(b) The average length of lines drawn by volunteers

(c) Data for volunteer 2 does not support this conclusion.
Results are from a small / unrepresentative sample / sample size was very small / number of attempts per volunteer was very small

(d) Repeat the experiment / use more attempts per person / increase sample size / make sure both left- and right-handed people are sampled

(e) Have a straight edge fixed on top of the paper to ensure the volunteer draws a straight line; use a backed chair, not a stool, to make the volunteer always maintain the same start posture; use a computer model instead of the physical apparatus to ensure conditions can be controlled more effectively.

Answers to End of Unit 3 Questions

Section A

1. D

2. A

3. B

4. D

5. D

Section B

1. Biomes

2. Light intensity, temperature, competition, parasitism, predation

3. (a) D

   (b) Some energy is lost as heat or wastes (urine, faeces); animals may move to a different environment and so their energy is not available to the next level feeders

4. An organism whose presence or absence indicates the level of pollution in a habitat

5. (a) 12 (experimental chamber) ; 20 (control chamber)

   (b) (i)   To prevent insects entering the chamber

      (ii)   Allows plants to photosynthesise

      (iii)   To mix air and sulphur dioxide

      (iv)   To draw air over the plants and out of the chamber

   (c) 1.   Make sure no soil was included in the weighing

      2.   Make sure all the plant tissue was weighed / continue drying until the mass was constant

(d) 1. Exposure time for both chambers must be the same

2. Temperature for both chambers should be constant

3. Plants should be at the same initial stage of growth

(e) In their normal environment, plants would not be exposed to constant bright light
Use timer to make cycle of light/dark the same as would be the case in the normal environment of the plants

(f) By repeating the experiment / using many more plants

(g) No
The results do not allow any statement about the cause of the different growths of the plants in the two different chambers